60—

THE HAWKS OF NORTH AMERICA

AMERICAN or BALD EAGLE
Adult perched, immature in flight

THE HAWKS OF
NORTH AMERICA

THEIR FIELD IDENTIFICATION
AND FEEDING HABITS

by

JOHN BICHARD MAY

Illustrated by

ALLAN BROOKS

and

ROGER TORY PETERSON

Published by

THE NATIONAL ASSOCIATION OF AUDUBON SOCIETIES

1775 Broadway, New York City

1935

Engraved, Printed and Bound
by
The Moore Press Incorporated
New York City

A STATEMENT OF POLICY

The Board of Directors of the National Association of Audubon Societies has adopted the following expression of policies with relation to the preservation of Hawks:

ONE

We oppose the extermination of any species of bird; in this we include Hawks and Owls without exception.

TWO

We advocate protection, under all conditions, of rare Hawks, such as the Duck Hawk, and of beneficial Hawks and Owls, such as the Broad-winged Hawk and the Barn Owl.

THREE

We oppose the killing of Hawks and Owls, other than those individual birds known to be damaging property.

FOUR

We condemn bounties, Hawk campaigns and general Hawk shoots because: First: They result in the indiscriminate killing, without regard to merit, as great numbers of hunters are not qualified to tell one species of Hawk or Owl from another. Second: They put many hunters in the field outside the regular shooting season, making law enforcement more difficult. Third: If control is needed, such work should be conducted only by properly qualified authorities.

FIVE

We are opposed to the pole trap because it is cruel and indiscriminate.

SIX

We aim—First: Through educational methods, to create greater popular appreciation of the aesthetic, scientific and economic value of Hawks and Owls. Second: To combat the constant propaganda which encourages their destruction. Third: To work for the enactment of laws for their protection.

NATIONAL ASSOCIATION OF AUDUBON SOCIETIES
For the Protection of Wild Birds and Animals

FOREWORD

Few birds have so appealed to the imagination of mankind as have the Eagles, Falcons, Hawks and their allies. From time immemorial they have figured prominently in the folklore and in the literature of all nations. Wise King Solomon once observed that among the many things "too wonderful to understand" was "the way of an Eagle in the air."

It is evident that all through the centuries something of this same sense of wonderment and admiration for the Eagle must have existed in the popular mind, for, to many nations, including Imperial Rome, it was a symbol of valor and of power; while the Bald Eagle is today the emblem of our own National Independence.

In like manner, though in varying degree, other members of this striking group of birds have aroused the special interest and admiration of mankind by reason of their remarkable grace and beauty or their prowess — from the majestic Condor and Lämmergeier to the dashing and spirited Falcons, which were the special delight of kings and knights in those far-off romantic days of chivalry when falconry was among the most popular and engaging of all field sports.

The time came, however, when there developed in the public mind a strong prejudice against raptorial birds, the assumption being that they were largely responsible for the rapid decline in the supply of wild game birds, as well as inimical to the interests of poultry raisers and game breeders. Game protective officials and sportsmen generally agreed with this point of view.

In 1893 the United States Department of Agriculture published a book which made conservation history: "The Hawks and Owls of the United States in their Relation to Agriculture," by Dr. A. K. Fisher. This made clear the desirability to the farmer of protecting the majority of these birds, covering, as it did, a scientific study of the feeding habits of 32 species of Hawks and 17 species of Owls, based on the examination of the stomach contents of 2,690 birds. It followed Dr. B. H. Warren's "Report on the Birds of Pennsylvania with Special Reference to the Food-Habits" (1890), and has been supplemented by much local research and published data.

Encouraged and fortified by this material, the United States Bureau of Biological Survey and the National Association of Audubon Societies and other agencies have been busy for more than thirty years in seeking to create a better public appreciation of these magnificent birds. Active campaigns have resulted in securing a measure of protective legislation, and at the present time thirty-one states have laws protecting some of the more obviously useful Hawks. The National Association of Audubon Societies has distributed a very large amount of its own literature and that of other organizations and individuals. Its officers and field agents, in their lecture work, have continually emphasized the economic value of Hawks and have *sent out, through the press, numerous articles on the need of hawk preservation. So deeply seated is the prejudice against these birds, however, that change in public sentiment from the days when every farmer or poultry raiser looked upon a Hawk as a menace to his livelihood, has come but slowly; and the enforcement of laws for the protection of Hawks has not been satisfactory. Protective statutes, secured only by great labor, remain unenforced in many states because most game wardens decline to make arrests for their infraction, and if arrests are made, magistrates often have refused to impose fines. An ever increasing body of scientifically trained game experts, such men as Stoddard, Errington and Leopold, have made clear the danger of further upsetting the balance of nature by killing off the winged Raptors, and many of the better educated farmers and the more thoughtful of the sportsmen are becoming cognizant of this danger.*

Two very important changes have altered the picture in the last few decades: first, the rapid and ever increasing numbers of gunners armed with weapons of high efficiency; and, second, the influence of game farms and game breeders, which have become a new and important factor. The British system of Pheasant and game propagation has brought into operation hundreds of game farms often under the administration of imported keepers who have applied the "vermin control" methods that have decimated the Eagles, Hawks and Kites of the British Isles. Game birds are frequently raised in large numbers, in pens without overhead protection or cover under which to take refuge. Many Hawks or Owls, normally beneficial in their feeding habits, are attracted to such places and are shot at every opportunity or caught by pole or by baited traps. At most game farms Hawks are killed at any and all times without regard to species or to actual damage done. In fact, comparatively few people have studied the Hawks sufficiently to be able to distinguish one species from another.

Coupled with this condition, far reaching propaganda is carried on by some sporting and commercial interests urging the killing of "vermin" of all kinds. Blame for the alarming decrease of game has been frequently and unjustly laid at the door of the winged predators. This propaganda has encouraged those gunners who believe that "the only good Hawk is a dead Hawk" and who wish to kill them on sight. Some of the sporting magazines and clubs, catering to popular feeling, have urged the shooting of Hawks in the off season for target practice, or on the ground that such killing will increase game; overlooking completely, the economic unwisdom of such a course, as demonstrated by scientific evidence. Not only do individual farmers and hunters shoot these birds, but organizations conduct campaigns for their destruction and various State Conservation Departments offer bounties on their heads. These combined agencies have been responsible for the rapid diminution of many species.

As part of an intensive educational campaign in behalf of these birds, we are publishing this book. Dr. John B. May, who has served as Director of Ornithology of the Massachusetts Department of Agriculture, was selected as the author because of his qualifications as an economic ornithologist and his keen personal interest in the birds of prey. The content is limited to means of identification of the various species and to their food habits.

Maps are included showing the geographical occurrence of the species, and in some cases both present and former breeding ranges and wintering areas are shown. It is not to be inferred that all species are common or even of regular occurrence over all the breeding areas indicated; how they are distributed is treated in the text.

T. GILBERT PEARSON
President Emeritus

TABLE OF CONTENTS

LIST OF ILLUSTRATIONS

CLASSIFICATION

of the

DIURNAL BIRDS OF PREY

From the Check-List of North American Birds, Fourth Edition, 1931

CLASS *Aves.* Birds.

SUBCLASS *Neornithes.* Typical Birds.

SUPERORDER *Neognathae.* Non-Struthious Birds.

ORDER *Falconiformes.* Birds of Prey.

SUBORDER *Cathartae.* American Vultures.

FAMILY *Cathartidae.* American Vultures.

Turkey Vulture, *Cathartes aura septentrionalis* WIED.
Black Vulture, *Coragyps atratus atratus* (MEYER).
California Condor, *Gymnogyps californianus* (SHAW).

SUBORDER *Falcones.* Kites, Hawks, Buzzards, Eagles, Harriers, and Falcons.

SUPERFAMILY *Falconoidea.* Hawks and Allies.

FAMILY *Accipitriidae.* Kites, Hawks, and Allies.

SUBFAMILY *Elaninae.* White-tailed Kites.

White-tailed Kite, *Elanus leucurus majusculus* BANGS and PENARD.

SUBFAMILY *Perninae.* Honey Buzzards and Swallow-tailed Kites.

Swallow-tailed Kite, *Elanoides forficatus forficatus* (LINNAEUS).

SUBFAMILY *Milvinae.* True Kites.

Mississippi Kite, *Ictinia misisippiensis* (WILSON).
Everglade Kite, *Rostrhamus sociabilis plumbeus* RIDGWAY.

SUBFAMILY *Accipitriinae.* Bird Hawks.

Eastern Goshawk, *Astur atricapillus atricapillus* (WILSON).
Western Goshawk, *Astur atricapillus striatulus* RIDGWAY.
Sharp-shinned Hawk, *Accipiter velox velox* (WILSON).
Cooper's Hawk, *Accipiter cooperi* (BONAPARTE).

SUBFAMILY *Buteoninae.* Buzzards and Eagles.

Eastern Red-tailed Hawk, *Buteo borealis borealis* (GMELIN).
Florida Red-tailed Hawk, *Buteo borealis umbrinus* BANGS.
Krider's Hawk, *Buteo borealis krideri* HOOPES.
Western Red-tailed Hawk, *Buteo borealis calurus* CASSIN.
Harlan's Hawk, *Buteo borealis harlani* (AUDUBON).
Northern Red-shouldered Hawk, *Buteo lineatus lineatus* (GMELIN).
Florida Red-shouldered Hawk, *Buteo lineatus alleni* RIDGWAY.
Insular Red-shouldered Hawk, *Buteo lineatus extimus* BANGS.
Texas Red-shouldered Hawk, *Buteo lineatus texanus* BISHOP.
Red-bellied Hawk, *Buteo lineatus elegans* CASSIN.
Broad-winged Hawk, *Buteo platypterus platypterus* (VIEILLOT).
Swainson's Hawk, *Buteo swainsoni* BONAPARTE.
Zone-tailed Hawk, *Buteo albonotatus* KAUP.
Sennett's White-tailed Hawk, *Buteo albicaudatus hypospodius* GURNEY.
Short-tailed Hawk, *Buteo brachyurus* VIEILLOT.

American Rough-legged Hawk, *Buteo lagopus s.-johannis* (GMELIN).
Ferruginous Rough-leg, *Buteo regalis* (GRAY).
Harris's Hawk, *Parabuteo unicinctus harrisi* (AUDUBON).
Mexican Goshawk, *Asturina plagiata plagiata* SCHLEGEL.
Mexican Black Hawk, *Urubitinga anthracina anthracina* (LICHTENSTEIN).
American Golden Eagle, *Aquila chrysaëtos canadensis* (LINNAEUS).
Gray Sea Eagle, *Haliaeetus albicilla* (LINNAEUS).
Northern Bald Eagle, *Haliaeetus leucocephalus alascanus* TOWNSEND.
Southern Bald Eagle, *Haliaeetus leucocephalus leucocephalus* (LINNAEUS).
Steller's Sea Eagle, *Thallasoaëtus pelagicus* (PALLAS).

SUBFAMILY *Circinae.* Harriers.
Marsh Hawk, *Circus hudsonius* (LINNAEUS).

SUBFAMILY *Pandioninae.* Ospreys.
American Osprey, *Pandion haliaëtus carolinensis* (GMELIN).

FAMILY *Falconidae.* Caracaras and Falcons.
SUBFAMILY *Polyborinae.* Caracaras.
Audubon's Caracara, *Polyborus cheriway auduboni* CASSIN.
Guadalupe Caracara, *Polyborus lutosus* RIDGWAY.

SUBFAMILY *Falconinae.* Falcons.
White Gyrfalcon, *Falco rusticolus candicans* GMELIN.
Asiatic Gyrfalcon, *Falco rusticolus uralensis* SEWERTZOV and MENZBIER.
Black Gyrfalcon, *Falco rusticolus obsoletus* GMELIN.
Prairie Falcon, *Falco mexicanus* SCHLEGEL.
Peregrine Falcon, *Falco peregrinus peregrinus* TUNSTALL.
Duck Hawk, *Falco peregrinus anatum* BONAPARTE.
Peale's Falcon, *Falco peregrinus pealei* RIDGWAY.
Aplomado Falcon, *Falco fusco-coerulescens septentrionalis* TODD.
Eastern Pigeon Hawk, *Falco columbarius columbarius* LINNAEUS.
Black Pigeon Hawk, *Falco columbarius suckleyi* RIDGWAY.
Richardson's Pigeon Hawk, *Falco columbarius richardsoni* RIDGWAY.
Western Pigeon Hawk, *Falco columbarius bendirei* SWANN.
Merlin, *Falco aesalon aesalon* TUNSTALL.
Kestrel, *Falco tinnunculus tinnunculus* LINNAEUS.
Eastern Sparrow Hawk, *Falco sparverius sparverius* LINNAEUS.
Desert Sparrow Hawk, *Falco sparverius phalaena* (LESSON).
San Lucas Sparrow Hawk, *Falco sparverius peninsularis* MEARNS.
Little Sparrow Hawk, *Falco sparverius paulus* (HOWE and KING).

INTRODUCTION
The Hawks of North America

Spring o' the Year! From high overhead there comes a clear and thrilling whistle, *"kee-you, kee-you."* You search and search, following the distant sound, and at last you see almost lost against the soft blue of the sky, two tiny broad-winged atoms that scarcely seem like birds, so far are they above the vernal landscape. You watch them dizzily as they circle and dip, the wide pinions seemingly motionless except when one of the wheeling birds banks too steeply against the wind, or the two birds come together for a moment and tumble over and over in mock combat.

"A pair of Hen Hawks," you say. Yes, but are they? Do they eat hens, and are you sure they do, or are you merely taking hearsay evidence and condemning them without fair trial? Do you realize that most Hawks, in spite of the widespread prejudice against the members of this group of birds, should be classed among the best friends of the farmer because of their destruction of injurious rodents and other pests, and that very few Hawks ever molest poultry? This volume has been prepared in the hope that by presenting the facts it may arouse a more friendly interest in these generally unappreciated and maligned birds, through a better knowledge of their real habits and their place in the economy of Nature.

What is a Hawk?

Just what do we mean when we call a bird a "Hawk"? To the average uninformed farmer, a Hawk is a robber of poultry yards; to the gunner, sportsman and game breeder, "vermin" to be ruthlessly destroyed; to the ammunition manufacturer and sporting goods dealer, an unprotected bird and therefore another "target"; to the biologist, a wonderful example of adaptation for life in a certain definite niche, a check upon harmful rodents, a control against the over-production of normally useful creatures, and an invaluable instrument in preserving what is known as "the balance of nature"; to the vast and rapidly increasing army of nature lovers and amateur bird students, one of the finest and most interesting forms of bird life, worthy of protection at all times.

For the purposes of this volume, a "Hawk" is any member of the order of birds called by the ornithologists *"Falconiformes"* or the Diurnal Birds of Prey. In this order are included such widely differing groups as the swift-flying Falcons, the sluggishly soaring Buteos or Buzzard Hawks, the graceful Kites, the lordly Eagles, the carrion-eating Vultures, and the true bird Hawks or Accipiters. James Lee Peters, in his "Check-List of the Birds of the World" (1931), recognizes about two hundred and ninety species among the *Falconiformes*, widely distributed throughout the entire globe with the exception of the extremes of the polar axis. In the fourth edition of the "Check-List of North American Birds" (1931), the American Ornithologists' Union committee includes thirty-seven living and one extinct species in the region covered by that volume, North America north of Mexico but including Lower California, and these are the species considered in this present book. Several of these species have been divided into various geographical races or subspecies, the American Sparrow Hawk, *Falco sparverius*, for example, being assigned twenty-three races ranging from the upper Yukon region in North America to Tierra del Fuego at the extreme tip of South America, though limited to the Western Hemisphere, while others, like the Rough-legged Hawk and Gyrfalcon, are circumpolar in distribution, and our Osprey or Fish Hawk is found in representative races on all the continents and many of the islands of the globe.

It is evident that Hawks must play an important role in Nature or they would not be found in such large numbers of species and so widely distributed, but until a comparatively few years ago Man had very little conception of what that part might be. Many myths had sprung up about them in different countries, and they had long been recognized as symbolic of courage and rapacity. Eagles were carried on the standards of the Roman legionaries, Hawks' wings decorated the helmets of the Norse sea-rovers, and Eagle feathers formed the war-bonnets of North American Indians. Today conventionalized Eagles are found on the coats-of-arms of many nations including the United States of America.

While much of Europe was still inhabited by uncivilized savages, Hawks of various species were being trained by Asiatics to assist in the hunt, and later falconry became the sport of the ruling classes in the Age of Chivalry. The art of rearing young birds and of capturing and training old ones was thoroughly understood, but little was accurately recorded regarding their actual habits in the wild state. Today this is greatly changed and we have accumulated a very considerable amount of data on the habits of these birds, upon which we may now make a fair estimate of their economic importance in the great scheme of Nature.

Decrease in Numbers

Hawks are pre-eminently meat-eaters, devourers of mammals, birds, insects and other forms of animal life, that they themselves may live. Because *some* of them undeniably kill and eat songbirds, game or poultry, from time immemorial undiscriminating Man has sentenced them *all* to death on sight, and despite the studies of conscientious and impartial scientists, the unreasoning prejudice still persists almost undimmed. Any keen observer of wild life, who has spent many seasons in the field, is well aware of the indisputable fact that our Hawks, taken as a group, are progressively diminishing in numbers, as the result of their long-continued persecution, and this observation holds true of every species with very few exceptions. Among our North American species, the Turkey Vulture and Black Vulture, which are not generally considered as "Hawks" by the layman, and which are valued in many places as scavengers, are holding their own in numbers or perhaps increasing in some localities. The widely distributed Sharp-shinned and Cooper's Hawks are decreasing but slowly, in spite of the fact that they are among the few species of hawks which feed almost entirely upon feathered prey, and therefore are largely to blame for the bad reputation which is fastened upon their tribe. Practically all other species, especially the two Eagles, Swainson's Hawk and the Ferruginous Rough-leg, have diminished with increasing rapidity within recent years. Several of them, in the opinion of many competent ornithologists, are in actual danger of extermination, at least as far as the United States and Canada are concerned, unless prompt and effective action is taken to protect them from their undeserved persecution. Among the latter species are the dainty and graceful little White-tailed Kite, an absolutely harmless bird of great beauty and interest, now found only in a few restricted localities; the equally beautiful and unique Swallow-tailed Kite; the very local and highly specialized Everglade Kite; the Red-bellied Hawk of the Pacific States; the Short-tailed Hawk of southern Florida; the great California Condor, the largest bird known to breed in North America.

Even the Bald Eagle, commonly considered the National Bird of the United States, and therefore deserving of protection for sentimental reasons, if for no others, has already disappeared from a great portion of its former haunts and is threatened with extermination as a nesting bird over a large part of the United States, as shown by the map contained in this book. In many areas where it still nests, it is greatly reduced in numbers, even in Canada, along the Great Lakes and on the Atlantic seaboard; it can be said to be common only in Florida and parts of Alaska and British Columbia. Although protected by law in 31 states, Eagles are often killed illegally, and rarely are prosecutions made even though full reports of the killing appear in the public press. In other states, Eagles have no legal protection and in some places there has even been an effort by the game commissioners and some "conservation" organizations to destroy these birds; or, as in Alaska, a bounty has been paid for their slaughter.

If any think that the danger to these species is overdrawn and exaggerated, they should remember the Guadalupe Caracara, a carrion-eating member of the Hawk tribe which has become extinct within very recent years, a victim of Man's greed and thoughtlessness, and they should also consider the experience of Great Britain, where of late the Gray Sea Eagle, Osprey, Marsh Harrier, Hen Harrier, Honey Buzzard and Red Kite have all either disappeared entirely as breeding species or are in very grave danger of extirpation. In North America we have already completely exterminated the Passenger Pigeon, Great Auk, Labrador Duck, Heath Hen, and probably Eskimo Curlew, birds which were largely killed for food; we decimated the Snowy Egret, Roseate Spoonbill, Least Tern and others merely for our personal adornment and the enrichment of the millinery trade; the Ivory-billed Woodpecker, Whooping Crane and Trumpeter Swan have almost disappeared before the spread of "civilization"; we may have waited too long before attempting to save the Condor, the White-tailed Kite and the Short-tailed Hawk, but the effort should be made, and made at once, before it is definitely too late. Many of our Hawks have already so diminished in numbers that they cannot be economically important throughout most of their natural habitat, and they now have, alas, the interest of rarity to add to their other attractions for the bird lover, the scientist and the conservationist.

Of course there are many different agencies which have contributed to this alarming reduction in our Hawk population, some of which are very wide-reaching and have affected many other forms of wild life and over which Man has little or no power of control. Most Hawks probably have few natural enemies, some of the smaller species being preyed upon by the larger Hawks and Owls, and occasionally a feathered predator is the victim of a furred one like a fox or a member of the weasel tribe. Parasites and disease may take their toll but of this we know little. Tempestuous weather may sometimes force even these powerful fliers far from land and cause their destruction (our only record of the Gray Sea Eagle south of Greenland is that of a bird which alighted in an exhausted condition on a steamer off Nantucket Lightship, Massachusetts, November 14, 1914, many hundreds of miles from its normal habitat, and our Swallow-tailed Kite has been recorded in Europe). This loss from natural enemies and from the elements would probably be fully taken care of by the normal reproduction rate, but Man has thrown his weight against the balance of nature, and serious results are likely to occur whenever this equilibrium is disturbed. Our predatory birds have undoubtedly a definite place to fill in our natural economy, and until we know much more than we do about the interrelations of our wild creatures, as a practical consideration we should be very solicitous not to allow any species to disappear entirely from our native fauna.

The recent acceleration in the rate of decrease of these birds is due solely to Man's influence. The spread of cultivation, with our steadily increasing population, has eliminated as breeding places many locations where Hawks formerly were found. This is perhaps unavoidable. But modern methods of hunting have improved much more rapidly than a knowledge of the habits and value of our birds has been disseminated. The automobile carries us far afield and high powered ammunition spreads destruction. Misdirected "protective" measures about poultry yards and game farms, such as the use of the nefarious "pole-trap" with its cruel and indiscriminate slaughter of (mostly) innocent victims, account for many deaths among our more beneficial Hawks while almost useless in the control of the few harmful varieties. Private and even governmental campaigns for the eradication of rodent pests through the use of poisons have often partly defeated their own purposes by their incidental slaughter of the very Hawks and Owls which are most useful as destroyers of injurious mammals. And private greed has gone even farther in the offering of bounties and the sponsoring of so-called "vermin shoots," which usually result in the killing of beneficial species. Control of certain species of Hawks, like the Goshawk, Cooper's Hawk and Sharp-shin, may sometimes seem necessary, but promiscuous slaughter should no longer be permitted in civilized countries, and such unselective methods as the use of poisons or of the atrocious pole-trap and the offering of bounties should be absolutely outlawed. Control, if considered necessary under special conditions, should only be undertaken by properly qualified and authorized persons, such as state or federal game wardens, and should never be allowed in the hands of the general public.

Study of Feeding Habits

Popular opinion and scientific research often differ markedly, and the feeding habits of our Hawks are among the things which recent investigations have revealed as at odds with common beliefs. Up to about forty years ago, most people divided the diurnal birds of prey (omitting the scavenging Vultures) into only two classes, namely "Hen Hawks" and "Chicken Hawks." All such Hawks were believed to feed largely upon poultry or small domestic animals, and every man's hand was turned against them, with bounties placed upon their heads in many cases. A few scientists of inquiring mind had begun to study the actual feeding habits of these birds, however, and to report their findings, but the information was not widely disseminated nor generally recognized as of value. Then Dr. B. H. Warren (1890) published the results of a considerable number of examinations of the stomachs and crops of Pennsylvania Hawks, and this was followed in 1893 by Dr. A. K. Fisher's classic governmental report on "The Hawks and Owls of the United States in their Relation to Agriculture," based upon the study of nearly twenty-seven hundred stomachs of Hawks and Owls collected during a number of years and over a wide expanse of territory. This bulletin received widespread distribution and the more progressive and intelligent farmers began for the first time to distinguish between "Bird Hawks" such as the Goshawk, Sharp-shin, and Cooper's Hawk, and the decidedly beneficial "Mouse Hawks" and "Grasshopper Hawks."

About this time, also, amateur bird study, stimulated by the outdoor writings of such men as John Burroughs and Bradford Torrey, began to forge ahead by leaps and bounds, and the "bird lover" found in the sight of a soaring Red-tail or Red-shoulder, a dashing Falcon, or a majestic Eagle, an inspiration and a joy not found in the study of many of the smaller members of the feathered folk. Today, this interest is almost universal and what we may, for lack of a better term, call the "esthetic value" of these birds, is not lightly to be overlooked or forgotten. This "esthetic value" is an intangible thing, impossible to evaluate in cold dollars and cents, but very real to an ever increasing army of outdoor people. With our steadily augmenting population and our greater leisure, more and more discriminating men and women are learning to enjoy the out-of-doors, and are becoming acquainted with our bird neighbors. To the eager nature lover afield, there are few thrills which equal those caused by occasional contacts with the birds of prey, whether it be a glimpse of a Duck Hawk stooping with whistling wings in pursuit of a fast flying Pigeon or Shore Bird, a pair of Marsh Harriers tumbling like acrobats in their aerial courtship display, an Osprey plunging headlong into the waters of lake or bay, or perhaps best of all, the graceful evolutions of a Swallow-tailed Kite wheeling and plunging above some moss-draped southern cypress swamp. All such people view with a feeling of personal loss the rapid diminution in the numbers of these interesting creatures.

Dr. George Miksch Sutton, in an article in the Auk for April, 1929, states well the nature lovers' claims for the protection and preservation of these birds. Referring to the Duck Hawk or American Peregrine Falcon, he calls it "one of the swiftest, most nicely balanced and beautifully colored birds in existence.—The most perfect flying organism which Nature has yet evolved," and adds "a plea for the Duck Hawk's preservation may well center in a study of the deepest desires of the human race,—the desire for happiness, for beauty, for interesting experience. —The public must be brought to a realization of the fact that great beauty is to be found where mere prettiness does not exist; that the soaring of the wide-winged hawks, their discordant cries, their mottled plumage and gleaming eyes, are just as truly beautiful as the fluttering flight, cheerful songs and sweet faces of our smaller bird neighbors. Surely, an appreciation of the beauty and majesty of these birds of prey does not demand a special spiritual endowment of some sort!—Our deepest, most sincere reasons for protecting wild life are not, after all, based on economic values. If we can make the public sense the need for these magnificent creatures in every one's experience, the preservation of the birds of prey which are now too rare will become an important and fascinating feature of the wild-life conservation movement."

By many self-styled "practical" people, unfortunately, arguments such as Dr. Sutton offers are summarily dismissed as merely sentimental and unworthy their consideration. These people demand to be shown whether Hawks add or subtract from Man's income, and they are all too prone to condemn upon slight or hearsay evidence, and to refuse to accept the testimony of sincere bird students as to the beneficial actions of these birds. It is axiomatic with the liberty-loving American people that a person on trial is innocent until he is proved guilty, but we do not apparently carry this principle into our consideration of the birds of prey, which as a class are blackened by the reputation which only a few species deserve. To all such "practical" people and sceptics, we offer the paragraphs entitled "Feeding Habits" on the following pages, as giving impartially the voluminous data we have accumulated on the actual habits of these much discussed creatures.

The careful examination, by trained experts, of stomach and crop contents and of "pellets" (the undigested portions of their food ejected from the mouth by Raptors and some other species of birds), gives us a scientific basis for a report on the food of these birds which cannot be contraverted, in spite of certain recent attempts to belittle this method of obtaining information. Even a small fragment of bone in a pellet or among the partly digested remains in a bird's stomach may tell a most convincing story to the skilled biologist, especially when his investigations are accompanied by field studies of the bird's habits. Reports based solely on either field work or stomach examinations may in some cases be misleading but in the great majority of instances will be reliable. An observation related to me by Mr. John D. Smith of the Boston Society of Natural History illustrates the possibility of error in unchecked observations, for he once saw a Marsh Hawk feeding upon the carcass of a Buffle-head Duck. An examination of the stomach contents of this Harrier would have furnished excellent circumstantial evidence that the bird had committed the nefarious "crime" of killing and eating a game species of duck, but the actual facts as learned in the field proved that the duck had been caught accidentally in a trap set on the marsh, and that the Harrier was actually feeding upon what was already carrion. In another and published instance, a large Hawk was seen to enter a chicken yard and the irate farmer rushed for his gun and, as the Hawk rose with its prey, shot it, but to his surprise and chagrin, found that the supposed "Hen Hawk" had captured and was carrying away a large rat, a destructive creature which had probably accounted for the loss of numerous young chickens for which the innocent Hawk was unjustly blamed.

Most Hawks are opportunists and in the stress of hunger will eat almost anything edible, but as we accumulate a mass of data on the feeding habits of each species, we become better able to estimate its actual economic status. Of the thirty-eight species of diurnal birds of prey treated in this volume, the great majority are proved by our studies to be more beneficial than harmful in their relations to Man. Only six species, the Goshawk, Cooper's Hawk, Sharp-shinned Hawk, Golden Eagle, Duck Hawk and Pigeon Hawk, are ever seriously injurious to small birds, game or poultry, and the last three are nowhere abundant, while the Goshawk is a northern breeding bird which only occasionally invades well settled regions in any numbers. Some other species, like the Gyrfalcon, might do harm if they were common, but are actually too rare to be even considered from a purely economic point of view. A few others may be injurious under certain local conditions, such as the Marsh Hawk, which is generally considered beneficial or at least neutral in its feeding habits, but which at times may be rather destructive, and birds like the Red-tailed Hawk which as a species is decidedly beneficial but whose record is marred by the occasional depredations of individual birds. The damage to poultry and game done by these few species, however, is far outweighed by the benefit to agriculture and forestry performed by the great majority of the Hawks, through their destruction of tremendous quantities of injurious rodents and harmful insects.

The Ohio Journal of Science for September, 1932, contains an instructive contribution by Messrs. Baldwin, Kendeigh and Franks on "The Protection of Hawks and Owls in Ohio." It includes among other pertinent matters a compilation of all sight records of Hawks made in the state during a period of fifteen years by some seventeen experienced field observers, in a table showing the relative abundance of each of fourteen species of Hawks. "Almost exactly half of all hawks observed

Plate I VULTURES, HARRIERS, ACCIPITERS

Figure 1, California Condor. Figure 2, Turkey Vulture. Figure 3, Black Vulture. Figure 4, Marsh Hawk, adult male. Figure 5 American Goshawk. Figure 6, Sharp-shinned Hawk. Figure 7, Cooper's Hawk.

were Sparrow Hawks.—The Marsh Hawk ranks next, followed by the Red-shouldered and Red-tailed Hawks. These species are all decidedly beneficial to the farmer and sportsman. From the economic standpoint, more complaints have been lodged against the Cooper's, Sharp-shinned, Pigeon, Duck, and Goshawk than against any of the others. Yet these five species together make up only 8.7% of the entire hawk population in the state. The other 91.3% of the hawk population is made up of species generally recognized by scientists to be beneficial. In other words, there are in the state of Ohio, over ten recognized beneficial hawks to every one that may be considered less desirable. The good done by the ten over-balances by far the harm done by the one, and gives a clear indication of the great economic importance of hawks to the farmer and sportsman in Ohio." Similar studies in other states have shown a like preponderance of beneficial species.

In another table the above authors give an analysis of the total food consumption by all Hawks in Ohio. "The relative abundance of each species had to be considered so that the types of food consumed by the more abundant species may carry proportionately more weight than the type of food consumed by the less common species." This table shows that mice and other small mammals constitute about 35.7% of the total food of all Hawks in the state; poultry and game birds, only 4.8%; other birds, 16.9%; other vertebrates, 7.4%; insects, 30.3%; miscellaneous matter, 4.0%. With less than five per cent of their food poultry and game, why condemn all Hawks as "vermin"?

Hawks are apparently able to go for a considerable length of time without eating before they show any ill effects, and it seems quite likely that many adult Hawks do not make a real "kill" more than once in two or three days, as is indicated by the large number of "empty" stomachs found in any large series of examinations. On the other hand, growing birds require a very large amount of food and it is during the time when young Hawks are still in the nest that the greatest destruction of poultry, game and other birds takes place. Field studies, furthermore, have shown that many of the depredations on young poultry by individuals of ordinarily beneficial species of Hawks are committed by inexperienced immatures which apparently have not yet become adept in supporting themselves upon the rodents which more mature birds seem to prefer. Most of the "Hen Hawks" killed about poultry yards and game farms are young birds, less than a year old, which find young chicks in open fields very easy prey, and which have not as yet learned to avoid the habitations of their arch-enemy, Man.

Field Identification

Many of our Hawks, it must be admitted, are difficult of exact identification when viewed at some distance in the field. Closely related species sometimes show considerable superficial resemblances in coloration, particularly among the immature birds, and until one knows exactly what to look for in order to distinguish these similar appearing species, confusion is almost inevitable. Melanism, a dark

Plate II KITES, FALCONS, CARACARAS

Figure 1, *Everglade Kite, adult male.* Figure 2, *White-tailed Kite.* Figure 3, *Mississippi Kite.* Figure 4, *Swallow-tailed Kite.* Figure 5, *Prairie Falcon.* Figure 6, *Gyrfalcon.* Figure 7, *Duck Hawk.* Figure 8, *American Sparrow Hawk, male.* Figure 9, *Aplomado Falcon.* Figure 10, *Pigeon Hawk.* Figure 11, *Audubon's Caracara.*

phase, is common in many species, when ordinarily diagnostic markings are lost. As an example, "At a meeting of the best sportsmen of Monongahela County (West Va.) . . . to check up on a membership campaign, seven mounted specimens of birds were placed on a table and numbered. The eleven men present were asked to identify them without conversing with each other. The results follow:

NAME OF BIRD	NUMBER ANSWERING		
	Correct	Wrong	Did Not Know
Cooper's Hawk........................	1	5	5
Sparrow Hawk........................	5	None	6
Red-tail Hawk........................	6	2	3
Barred Owl...........................	2	3	6
Sharp-shinned Hawk...................	2	6	3
Red-shouldered Hawk.................	None	3	8
Cooper's Hawk........................	None	6	5

"Cooper's Hawk appeared twice in the group of birds. The first specimen was recognized by one man only and the other specimen not by a single man. Not one of the eleven recognized the Red-shouldered Hawk. Of the eleven men five did not name a single one of the seven birds correctly; one named five birds; two named three; two named two; one named one. These were real sportsmen; they had the birds in their hands; they were honest men; the birds are all common in the county. Does it seem likely that these men or other sportsmen could identify birds more nearly accurately if they were flying or if they were much farther away? Would these men be competent to destroy Hawks and Owls; or could the average sportsman be trusted to destroy them?" (*West Virginia Wild Life*).

There is often considerable variation in the size of members of the same species and, especially in the Accipitrine or "bird" Hawks, the females are often noticeably larger than the males. However, the beneficial and the harmful Hawks generally belong to different groups, the members of each of which have certain family resemblances and which permit of their classification as economically "good" or "bad" at a considerable distance, so that there should be little excuse for the killing of beneficial species, like the Kites and Buteos, "by mistake" for the bird-killing Accipiters. The four plates by Mr. Peterson are especially planned to show the distinguishing proportions of the outlines or "silhouettes" of the various hawks, as viewed from beneath when in flight, the position in which they are most likely to be seen by the average observer.

Identification in the field is rendered much easier if one learns to look for certain definite characteristics first, the details of color pattern following the first or "classifying" observations. The relative proportions between the length of the wings (the "spread" of the flying bird) and the length of the tail, furnish a clue of primary importance and these should be studied in relation to Mr. Peterson's plates.

Plate III BUTEONINE HAWKS

Figure 1, Ferruginous Rough-leg. Figure 2, American Rough-legged Hawk, light phase. Figure 3, American Rough-legged Hawk, dark phase. Figure 4, Red-tailed Hawk. Figure 5, Broad-winged Hawk. Figure 6, Short-tailed Hawk. Figure 7, Red-shouldered Hawk, immature. Figure 8, Red-shouldered Hawk, adult. Figure 9, Mexican Goshawk. Figure 10, Sennett's White-tailed Hawk. Figure 11, Swainson's Hawk. Figure 12, Zone-tailed Hawk. Figure 13, Harris's Hawk. Figure 14, Mexican Black Hawk.

If the bird under examination is in flight, as is so often the case with our wary predators, note particularly these relative proportions of the spread wings to the length of the tail (or the total length of the bird); whether the wings are broad or narrow, rounded or pointed at the tips; whether there is a "wrist-mark" or dark blotch near the bend of the wings, visible from below; whether the tail is square-ended or rounded, notched or forked, long or short, spread fan-like or held straight and closed; then of course note all conspicuous color masses. In this study of the flying Hawks, compare Plate III, the buteonine Hawks with their broad round-ended wings and comparatively short tails, with the narrow-winged Kites and Falcons of Plate II and the accipitrine Hawks of Plate I with their short round-ended wings and comparatively long tails. After one becomes familiar with these "group" characteristics, specific identification will be much easier.

Note further: Is the flight characterized by alternations of brief periods of flappings and sailings; is it rapid and direct, leisurely, or a zigzag quartering; does the bird soar with widely spread and almost motionless pinions, or does it occasionally hover in one spot with rapidly vibrating wings? Certain mannerisms of flight, such as the hovering in one spot of the Sparrow Hawk as distinguished from the Sharp-shinned Hawk; a similar habit of the Rough-leg as contrasted with the Red-tail; the skimming flight of the Marsh Hawk; the angle of the wings of the Turkey Buzzard when in flight; and the slight downward curve of the wings of the Osprey, frequently make field identification possible as far as the birds can be seen.

If the bird under observation is at rest, try to determine whether it is robust or slender of body; where the tips of the folded wings come in relation to the end of the tail (the wings of Accipiters come to about the upper third of the tail, those of Falcons to the lower third or near the end); whether the tail is long or short, barred or plain, square, rounded or notched.

Note the general color effect and any conspicuous masses of color. Are the under parts dark or light, streaked vertically or barred horizontally; is there a darker zone across the breast or belly; is there a conspicuous dark moustache, a light cheek, eyebrow or head, or a white area on the back near the base of the tail?

Where was the bird seen? Sitting motionless on some tall tree or jutting ledge, circling high over woods or mountainsides, beating low across marshes or meadow-lands, darting through thickets, or winging its way above a lake or river or an arm of the sea?

When was the bird seen? Was it a summer resident probably breeding nearby, a bird passing through in migration in spring or fall, or a winter straggler from colder northern regions? Was it sunning itself at high noon or quartering the fields at dusk? All of these and similar considerations may help in establishing the bird's identity and in making its future recognition more easy.

The largest number of closely related Hawks are found in the group of buteo-nine or "Buzzard" Hawks, and they are all characterized by their wide round-

Plate IV EAGLES, OSPREYS

Figure 1, American Golden Eagle, immature. Figure 2, Bald Eagle, adult. Figure 3, Bald Eagle, immature. Figure 4, Gray Sea Eagle, adult. Figure 5, American Osprey.

ended wings, rather short tails, and rather heavy bodies (see Plate III). The Eagles are very large Buteonines with proportionately longer wings (see Plate IV, Figures 1 to 4). The Falcons have long narrow pointed wings and fairly long tails (see Plate II, Figures 5 to 10). The accipitrine Hawks have short round-ended wings and long tails (see Plate I, Figures 5 to 7). The Kites have long narrow wings, except the Everglade Kite which has much the proportions of a Buteo (see Plate II, Figures 1 to 4). The Marsh Hawk, sole American representative of the Harriers, has long narrow wings, not as pointed as in the Falcon's, and it has a long tail, but its white rump, present in all ages and both sexes, is diagnostic (see Plate I, Figure 4). The Caracara and Osprey have characteristic outlines and are easily recognized at a considerable distance (see Plate II, Figure 11, and Plate IV, Figure 5). The Vultures are large, mostly black birds with small and inconspicuous naked heads (see Plate I, Figures 1 to 3).

The Protection of Hawks

Years ago men like Edward Howe Forbush in Massachusetts, W. DeWitt Miller in New York, W. E. Saunders in Ontario, and others, began to realize the dangerous decrease in the numbers of our so-called "birds of prey" and to agitate for their better protection. The National Association of Audubon Societies, under the leadership of its first president, William Dutcher and his successor, Dr. T. Gilbert Pearson, also recognized the condition and some of the earliest of its great series of educational leaflets were devoted to certain Hawks, while more recently it has published a number of special bulletins on this class of birds, and it has been very active in urging legislative action, both state and federal, for the preservation of these interesting and valuable creatures. Various other organizations, including the Brodie Club in Canada, The Emergency Conservation Committee of New York, and several local Audubon societies in the United States, have also been active in this field, in spite of the opposition of many game clubs and even state conservation departments. Within the past few years a special organization has been formed, the Hawk and Owl Society, with its primary objects the better appreciation and the protection of these maligned and persecuted birds. Thirty-one states have now on their statutes laws giving protection to certain Hawks (see Appendix) but enforcement is difficult and indeed they are but "dead letters" in many places. The deep-seated prejudices of generations are hard to overcome and there is still a great deal to be accomplished in arousing public opinion in favor of even a few of the really beneficial Hawks, and to save some of the rarer species from their threatened extermination. Legislation without popular support is insufficient; education and appreciation are necessary.

I am indebted to many ornithologists, both professional and amateur, for encouragement and assistance in preparing this volume. Among these were my friend and mentor the late Edward Howe Forbush; Dr. A. K. Fisher and W. L. McAtee of the Bureau of Biological Survey; the late W. DeW. Miller; W. E. Saunders and L. L. Snyder of Ontario; Warren F. Eaton, secretary of the Hawk and Owl Society; S. Gilbert Emilio; and others too numerous to mention. I am also indebted to Major Allan Brooks for many notes on field identification and feeding habits, and for his fine cooperation in the preparation of the colored plates for this book; also to Roger T. Peterson for his painstaking care in producing his paintings of Hawks in flight. The distribution maps are the work of Robert P. Allen of the National Association of Audubon Societies and are based upon the "ranges" as given in the fourth edition of the "Check-List" of the American Ornithologists' Union, with additions or corrections from various reliable sources. The manuscript has been critically read by Dr. Frank M. Chapman, who also has been kind enough to give careful attention to the selection of type, binding and other technical matters. And the deepest of appreciation is due to Mrs. Carll Tucker, for her very generous assistance in making the publication of "The Hawks of North America" financially possible.

JOHN BICHARD MAY.

Cohasset, Massachusetts,
March, 1935.

THE HAWKS OF NORTH AMERICA

THEIR FIELD IDENTIFICATION AND FEEDING HABITS

BLACK VULTURE, TURKEY VULTURE

Black Vultures at left, Turkey Vultures at right

THE VULTURES

The American Vultures are characterized by their large size, naked heads, and large but comparatively weak feet which lack the strong talons of most birds of prey. They feed almost exclusively upon carrion and are therefore entirely harmless and are often beneficial as scavengers.

TURKEY VULTURE

Cathartes aura septentrionalis Wied

Other Names. Buzzard, Turkey Buzzard, Carrion Crow, John Crow, Red-necked Buzzard.
—The name "Buzzard," commonly applied to this and the next species, is also
used by many when referring to the broad-winged Hawks of the genus *Buteo*.

The Turkey Vulture is a common and characteristic bird of much of the southern United States, but it is also occasionally found as far north as southern British Columbia and southern Ontario. There has been some discussion regarding its economic status, as it has been accused of carrying disease germs, and especially of spreading hog cholera, but A. H. Howell (1932) quotes the Florida State Board of Health as stating that "the virus of hog cholera is digested in the intestinal tract of Buzzards and the droppings of Buzzards fed on the flesh of hogs dead from cholera do not produce cholera when mixed in the food of hogs." T. G. Pearson (1919) says that Turkey Vultures are most useful birds as scavengers and "in many a southern city the Vultures constitute a most effective street-cleaning department." In appreciation of this characteristic the Turkey Vulture is in most places protected both by law and by public sentiment.

The Turkey Vulture is easily recognizable. At close range the rusty edges of the body feathers give the bird a brownish tinge but at a little distance it appears plain black. When perched it usually sits in a hunched position, the small naked head drawn in between the shoulders. Frequently it may be seen sitting with partly expanded wings, apparently enjoying the warm sunshine. When approached it often spreads its wings and holds them open for several seconds, or expands and folds them several times, before jumping into the air. When rising from the ground it usually hops or runs clumsily for a few yards and its first wing-beats are hurried and awkward, but when once fairly launched in flight it sweeps around in great circles, often climbing upward to great heights with hardly a movement of its long wings. When flying overhead the entire plumage appears black except the tail and the long flight feathers, which appear grayish in marked contrast to the darker under wing coverts and the body feathers. The tips of the first five or six primaries are distinctly separated like the fingers of a spread hand.

The Turkey Vulture is a master of easy effortless flight, sailing for hours at a time with set and motionless pinions, often at a tremendous elevation; when watching one with field glasses, I have been surprised to observe others high above, beyond the vision of the naked eye. When soaring, the wings are usually held bent slightly upwards, forming a distinct angle with the bird's body at the apex of the angle; the wings of the soaring Black Vulture are extended more nearly horizontally. The tail is usually held closed and shows, from below, a narrow and slightly wedge-shaped outline, the central feathers being longest. The small naked head is quite inconspicuous and is usually carried close to the shoulders unless the bird is closely scanning some object. As the bird glides downward it often careens from side to side without changing the relative positions of the wings and tail. Though usually silent, when disturbed at its feast of carrion, or when quarreling with its fellows, it occasionally utters a few low hissing sounds and croaks or grunts.

FEEDING HABITS

The Turkey Vulture feeds almost exclusively upon carrion, as is shown both by field studies and by all examinations of stomach contents. Its weak bill and feet are unfitted for capturing living prey or for tearing fresh meat.

Description—Length 26 to 32 inches, spread 68 to 72 inches. Adult: General plumage rusty black; under surface of flight feathers grayish in contrast to the darker wing coverts; head and neck bare of feathers, naked skin dull to bright red; bill red at base, whitish at tip; feet flesh colored or dirty grayish. Immature: Similar to adult but head dusky and more or less covered with whitish down.

Range—"Austral zones (chiefly) from southern British Columbia, central Alberta, Saskatchewan, southern Manitoba, Wisconsin, Michigan, northern Minnesota, southern Ontario, central New York, Connecticut, and New Jersey south to southern Lower California, the Gulf coast of the United States, and northern Mexico, breeding north at least to southern Michigan, northern Minnesota, southeastern New York and Connecticut. Winters throughout most of its regular range on the Atlantic slope but not north of the Ohio Valley, Nebraska, and California. Casual in northern Ontario, New England (north to New Hampshire and Maine), New Brunswick, and Newfoundland." (A. O. U.)

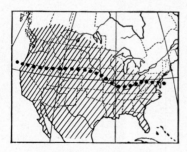

TURKEY VULTURE
Ruled Area—Breeding Range
Dotted Line—Northern Boundary
of Winter Range

Representative races occur in Central and South America.

THE VULTURES

BLACK VULTURE
Coragyps atratus atratus (Meyer)

Other Names. **Carrion** Crow, Jim Crow, Black Buzzard, Black Scavenger, Black-headed Buzzard.

The Black Vulture is of decided value as a scavenger. It is generally protected by law and by public opinion.

In most of its habits the Black Vulture resembles the Turkey Vulture but it may be easily distinguished. When perched or on the ground it appears heavier and shorter than the latter bird, with which it is often associated. All Vultures walk instead of hopping as is habitual with most Hawks. When in flight and viewed from below, the Black Vulture appears all black except for the outermost six or seven flight feathers which have a grayish or whitish appearance at the base, an excellent field mark. The wings are noticeably broader and shorter proportionately than those of the Turkey Vulture and the short square-ended tail projects but little beyond the line of the extended wings, while the feet sometimes may be seen extending beyond the end of the tail. The flight of the Black Vulture is less graceful than that of its associate and it cannot soar as easily and continuously but usually flaps its wings hurriedly a few times and then sails with its wings extended horizontally, renewing the motion of the wings at frequent intervals. The short tail is usually spread open like a fan, not closed as in the case of the Turkey Vulture, and it is so short as to give the impression of having been cut off abruptly. The two Vultures can be readily distinguished "at the limit of vision," in spite of their similarity of coloration, by a study of their relative proportions. The narrow and very long wings, narrow wedge-shaped tail, and the angle at which the wings are carried, make the Turkey Vulture unmistakable. The Black Vulture is a shorter, heavier appearing bird. The Turkey Vulture is only exceeded in spread of wings by the California Condor and the Eagles. The much larger Condor has a conspicuous area of pure white on the under surface of the wings anteriorly. The large fully feathered heads of the Eagles are conspicuous, in marked contrast to the small heads and "neckless" appearance of the Vultures. The Osprey approaches the Vultures in spread of wings but is largely brown above and white below. The melanistic phases of some of the large Hawks may cause confusion but they have larger and more noticeable heads, and when soaring their broad fan-shaped tails are prominent.

FEEDING HABITS

The Black Vulture's feeding habits are very similar to those of the Turkey Vulture and they are often found associated together at their feasts of carrion. J. J. Audubon (1840-1844) says "they feed on all sorts of flesh, fresh or putrid, whether of quadrupeds or birds, as well as on fish" and adds "I have observed

CALIFORNIA CONDOR

Adults at left and in flight, immature perched at right

them many times devouring young cormorants and herons in the nest" in Florida, and similar observations have been made by many others. O. E. Baynard (1909) says that the eggs and young in a colony of Yellow-crowned Night Herons in Florida were almost all destroyed by Black Vultures and that "hundreds of young pigs, lambs, etc.," are annually destroyed by this species, as well as young chickens. On the other hand A. T. Wayne (1910) says "I have never seen the Black Vulture attack living animals" in South Carolina.

Description—Length 23 to 27 inches, spread 54 to 60 inches. General plumage dull or glossy black; shafts of primaries white and webs dull grayish at base, forming a noticeably light area which is conspicuous in flight; head and neck bare of feathers and blackish in color; bill black at base, whitish at tip; legs grayish.

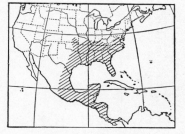

BLACK VULTURE
Ruled Area—Breeding Range

Range—"Tropical and Lower Austral zones from western Texas, Kansas, Missouri, southern Illinois, southern Indiana, Virginia, and southern Maryland south through the southern States to Mexico and Central America. Casual or accidental in southwestern Quebec, New Brunswick, Nova Scotia, Maine, Massachusetts, Indiana, southern Michigan, Ohio, New York, Arizona, and Jamaica." (A. O. U.)

A representative race is found in South America.

CALIFORNIA CONDOR

Gymnogyps californianus (SHAW)

Other Name. California Vulture.

The California Condor has been greatly reduced in numbers merely because it made a tempting target and its great quills were interesting souvenirs. It was never an abundant bird and was quite limited in its distribution. Today, because of its rarity, it is of no economic importance but it has a definite esthetic and sentimental value. *It should be rigorously protected* wherever it still lingers, as an interesting and unique addition to the wild scenery of its mountain haunts. Unless protective laws are promptly enacted and *enforced* and public opinion aroused for its preservation, it is probably doomed to early extinction, its predilection for carrion making it an easy victim for the poison baits of the wolf and coyote trapper. Every effort, therefore, should be made to prevent the use of such bait in the area where the Condor is still found.

The great California Condor is now so rare that only in a very few favored places may one even hope to have diligent search rewarded by a glimpse of this magnificent bird, our largest North American species, which, once seen, will never be forgotten. The adult is easily recognized in the field by its great size and by the extensive areas of pure white on the wings toward their forward edges. Young birds resemble Turkey Vultures both in outline and in coloration, but their expanse is one and a half or nearly two times that of the latter bird. Their straightforward flight is slow, steady and graceful, and they also soar majestically, at great heights, with little or no motion of the wings. When soaring the tips of the wings curve upward "but the inner half is decidedly arched, so that the wing, when viewed from front or rear, forms a very symmetrical sigmoid curve." The inner half of the wing of the Turkey Vulture is straight or curves slightly upward. The tail of the Condor is usually spread fan-like when soaring. On the ground the Condor is awkward and clumsy; when taking off in flight it is obliged to hop or run clumsily for some distance before it can clear the ground. Large Eagles approach small Condors in spread of wings but their fully feathered heads and necks are more conspicuous than the naked heads of the Vultures, and this point alone is sufficient to identify them.

FEEDING HABITS

The principal food of the California Condor is carrion, but it occasionally captures living prey. Although it is accused by shepherds of killing young lambs and even sickly sheep, there is very little reliable evidence against the bird and the report is probably exaggerated. Sickly sheep seldom survive on the open range and their destruction and subsequent conversion into food for Vultures may eliminate them as sources of contagion for other sheep. As stated above, the Condor is too rare today to be an economic factor.

Description—The largest of all North American land birds. Length 43 to 55 inches, spread 8½ to 11 feet. Adult: Head and neck bare of feathers, skin yellow or orange and red; the rather large bill whitish; body plumage, wings and tail sooty black, except upper wing coverts and secondaries which are more or less edged with white, and the pure white axillars and under wing coverts; a ruff of pointed feathers at the base of the neck. Immature: Neck covered with more or less sooty grayish down; bill and exposed skin blackish; feathers of upper parts have a brownish edging which gives a scaled effect at short range; white under wings wanting.

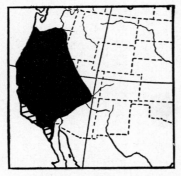

CALIFORNIA CONDOR
Ruled Area—Breeding Range
Black Area—Former Breeding Range

Range—"California west of the Great Basin and desert regions, and northwestern Lower California; formerly from Tehama County south along the western slopes of the Sierra Nevada and throughout the Coast Ranges from Humboldt County to the Mexican line; now restricted to the Coast Ranges from San Benito County to Los Angeles County and the Sierra San Pedro Martir of northwestern Lower California. Has been reported casually or formerly from southeastern California, Oregon and Washington." (A. O. U.) "In the interior to southern Utah" (A. O. U. 1886). "Formerly north to the Columbia River." (Peters.)

6

THE KITES

The Kites are generally distinguished by their long narrow wings and their light and graceful flight, though the Everglade Kite has wider wings much resembling those of a typical Buteo. They are absolutely harmless in their feeding habits, birds being practically unknown in their dietary. There is no possible excuse for killing such harmless and easily recognized birds, for their feeding habits have been well known since the days of Wilson and Audubon.

WHITE-TAILED KITE
Elanus leucurus majusculus Bangs and Penard

Other Names. Black-shouldered Kite, Black-winged Kite, White Hawk.

The White-tailed Kite is not only a harmless and beautiful bird but it is a potentially valuable destroyer of injurious insects. It has diminished rapidly, however, and is today in very real danger of complete extirpation in the United States, where it is now very rare and local. *An earnest and immediate effort should be made to arouse public opinion, through education, to save the pitiful remnant of this beautiful species before it has completely vanished,* and to increase its numbers if possible. Only education can accomplish what laws have failed to do.

This very attractive little bird is noticeable for its confiding and gentle disposition as well as for the beauty and softness of its coloring. When hunting, it flies much in the open, where its method resembles that of the Marsh Hawk, as it beats back and forth across the fields and marshes with slow but buoyant flight, or, with lightly fanning wings, wide-spread tail, and dangling legs, hovers briefly over its prey, then, raising its wings over its body until they almost meet, drops like a plummet upon its unsuspecting quarry. Gayle Pickwell (1930) gives a very complete study of this interesting species and states that "as far as one can see the faintest outline of its silhouette a Kite is identifiable. No other bird flies so characteristically with wings, whether in beat or sail, at the peculiar angle that a Kite maintains. This is not a set of the wings in a straight line such as a large hawk or gull maintains, but that with wings slightly raised and downcurving at the tips. No other hawk flies like this.—The leg-dangling habit—is one of their most conspicuous oddities.—When prey is seen the bird 'stands' with wings quiet if the wind is moving sufficiently to permit it to 'kite'—or beats the wings slowly from an angle well above the back. If it stoops it makes no falcon drop of lightning speed with wings drawn in to a thin wedge along the sides of the body, but keeps them up in a V angle above and slips down with legs dangling and at a speed which one would never guess was more than enough to catch a snail."

WHITE-TAILED KITE

Adults at left and in flight, immature at right

While its flight is easy and graceful, it is not particularly rapid and it lacks the dash and spirit of many other Hawks. It frequently changes not only the direction of its flight but the altitude. At times it sails in easy circles at a moderate elevation, or perches on a dead branch and watches for its prey. When it first alights its tail is often tilted several times after the manner of the Sparrow Hawk. When perched, the white head and breast of the adult, with the black shoulder patch contrasting with the gray mantle, are good field marks. W. H. Hudson (1920) says that "when seen at a distance its snow-white plumage and buoyant flight give it a striking resemblance to a gull. Its wing-power is indeed marvelous. It delights to soar—during a high wind—rising and falling alternately, and, at times, seeming to abandon itself to the fury of the gale, is blown away like thistle-down, until, suddenly recovering itself, it shoots back to its original position."

This species might possibly be mistaken at a distance for a male Marsh Hawk but the latter has dark tips to the wings, a white rump patch and a grayish tail with six to eight darker bars; the Kite has a black patch near the bend of the wings above and below, and a shorter unbarred white tail. The notes of the White-tailed Kite are described as a low plaintive whistle, quite pleasing to the ear; a sharp whistle at frequent intervals; a high slightly drawled *pee* given with a rising inflection; a low cackle like the Marsh Hawk's *kek, kek, kek*.

FEEDING HABITS

A. K. Fisher (1893) states that the food of the White-tailed Kite consists of "small snakes, lizards, frogs, and such insects as grasshoppers and beetles" and he quotes Audubon as saying that he found the remains of birds in two stomachs he examined, which Dr. Fisher remarks is "an experience no naturalist has shared with him as far as I know." Chester Barlow (1897) says their principal food is "gophers, field mice and wood rats, lizards, and probably in season a few grass-hoppers." W. K. Fisher (*mss.* notes, Bureau of Biological Survey, 1901) says that they catch large numbers of meadow mice in California. D. D. McLean (1928-a) saw one apparently capture a frog or small toad. Gayle Pickwell (1930) reports finding a freshly killed ground squirrel under a nest in California; he also found skulls of five meadow mice in eight pellets taken from a nest.

RESULTS OF EXAMINATIONS OF STOMACHS AND CROPS

Authority	Number Examined	Mam-mals	Poultry or Game	Other Birds	Other Vertebrates	Insects	Miscel-laneous	Empty
Fisher, A. K., 1893	1	1	0	0	0	0	0	0
Miller, Loye, 1926	1	1	0	0	0	0	0	0
Brooks, Allan, *in litt.*	2	1	0	0	0	0	0	1
Stoner, E. A., 1933	1	1	0	0	0	0	0	0
Pearson, T. G., *in litt.* . . .	1	1	0	0	0	0	0	0
Totals	6	5	0	0	0	0	0	1

SWALLOW-TAILED KITE
Adults

Description—Length 15 to 17 inches, spread about 40 inches. Adult: General color of upper parts pale bluish gray, fading to white on head; under parts white; a short black line over eye; wings long and pointed; upper wing coverts black, forming a conspicuous dark area at bend of wing which shows both when in flight and when perched; a smaller black patch on under surface of wing near the bend, showing in flight when seen from below; tail medium, square-ended or slightly notched, and all white except two central feathers which are gray; feet yellow-

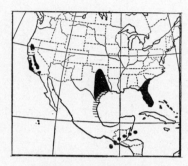

WHITE TAILED KITE
Ruled Area—Breeding Range
Black Area—Former Breeding Range
Dotted Line—Southern Boundary
of Winter Range

ish. Immature: Quite different in coloration, with cinnamon crown, brownish streaked back, rufous streaks on breast and under parts, white throat and forehead; tail grayish "with a darker subterminal band and a white tip" (A. C. Bent).

Range—"California west of the desert divides; from the upper Sacramento Valley and Humboldt County south to the San Diegan district and northern Lower California (rarely); also in Texas, Oklahoma and Florida south rarely to Guatemala. Casual in Louisiana, Illinois, Michigan, and South Carolina." (A. O. U.). Now extirpated in Oklahoma (Nice) and Florida (Bent). Accidental in Massachusetts (Forbush).

A representative race is found in South America.

SWALLOW-TAILED KITE
Elanoides forficatus forficatus (LINNAEUS)

Other Names. Forked-tailed Kite, Wasp Hawk, Swallow-tail.

The Swallow-tailed Kite is one of the most graceful and beautiful birds in North America. It is absolutely harmless in its feeding habits and in fact is potentially valuable as a destroyer of injurious insects, but it is becoming extremely rare and is threatened with early extermination unless public opinion can be aroused in its behalf and the people educated to protect it. *It should be given complete protection at all times.*

Observers are unanimous in their praise of this unique bird, whose striking markings of black and white, together with its long deeply forked tail, render it unmistakable. Dr. Frank M. Chapman says, "it possesses all the marvelous ease and grace of the swallow" while Rex Brasher states that "no other North American bird approaches it in the grace and beauty of its flight; the Duck Hawk alone equals it in speed. The former conveys the impression of lightness in the air; the latter, of power and impetuosity." William Brewster wrote "I hardly know a more attractive sight than that presented by one of these Kites playing about an opening in the woods. For a moment it floats motionless, as if suspended by an invisible

11

wire; the next, it glides close to the ground, crossing and recrossing every foot of space. The long thin wings, firmly set, cleave the air like knife-blades and the forked tail, spread to its fullest, is inclined to one side or the other as the bird changes its swift course. Finally rising to a level with the tree-tops it is gone as it came, like a beautiful vision." And Elliott Coues says, "marked among its kind by no ordinary beauty of form and brilliancy of color, the Kite courses through the air with a grace and buoyancy it would be vain to rival. By a stroke of the thin-bladed wings and a lashing of the cleft tail, its flight is swayed to this or that side in a moment, or instantly arrested. Now it swoops with incredible swiftness, seizes without a pause, and bears its struggling captive aloft, feeding from its talons as it flies; now it mounts in airy circles till it is a speck in the blue ether and disappears.—One cannot watch the flight of the Kite without comparing it with the thoroughbred racer."

The Swallow-tailed Kite usually nests among the branches of tall trees. Its call note is a shrill but rather feeble cry, somewhat resembling that of a Broad-winged Hawk and also likened by some authors to the *peet-weet* of the Spotted Sandpiper.

FEEDING HABITS

The food of the Swallow-tailed Kite consists largely of insects which it captures while on the wing, and of frogs, lizards and small snakes, which it picks up and eats while in flight, and it also drinks, like a huge Swallow, by dipping from the surface of quiet waters without checking its rapid course. Thomas Nuttall (1832) says they eat locusts and other large insects and have been seen destroying wasps' nests and eating both the adult insects and their larvae. Robert Owen (1860) states that they sometimes prey upon swarms of bees. Henry Nehrling (1882) says that they eat cotton worms and other insects, small snakes and lizards, but he has never seen one take a bird or small quadruped. A. K. Fisher (1893) gives it as his opinion that "it never molests small mammals or birds." A. T. Wayne (1910) states that the food consists of "grasshoppers, beetles, lizards, and small snakes."

RESULTS OF EXAMINATIONS OF STOMACHS AND CROPS

Authority	Number Examined	Mammals	Poultry or Game	Other Birds	Other Vertebrates	Insects	Miscellaneous	Empty
Audubon, J. J., 1831-1839 .	2	0	0	0	2	2	0	0
Aughey, Samuel, 1878 . . .	3	0	0	0	0	3	0	0
Warren, B. H., 1890	5	0	0	0	0	5	0	0
Fisher, A. K., 1893	6	0	0	0	3	6	0	0
Henning, C. F., 1896	1	0	0	0	1	1	0	0
Morgan, A. P., 1896	1	0	0	0	1	1	0	0
Bailey, B. H., 1918	1	0	0	0	0	1	0	0
Bur. Biol. Surv., 1893-1931 .	11	0	0	0	5	11	0	0
Totals	30	0	0	0	12	30	0	0

G. F. Simmons (1925) mentions "small snakes, lizards, chameleons, field mice, young Mockingbirds and Painted Buntings, bugs, flies, and wasps" but does not give his authority for including the birds. E. H. Forbush (1927) says, "large insects are taken chiefly—while on the wing, either high in air or sweeping along the surface of the ground, but it sometimes alights and walks about in pursuit of grasshoppers" and he says that its food includes "eggs of reptiles and there is one instance recorded by Dr. Rufus Hammond where an individual had swallowed some whole eggs of the Catbird."

Description—Wings very long and thin; tail very deeply forked, the outer feathers being about eight inches longer than the others. Length 19 to 25.5 inches, spread about 45 to 50 inches. Adult: Head, neck, rump, and lower parts including under wing coverts and under tail coverts, white; back, wings (except under wing coverts and parts of tertiaries), upper tail coverts, and tail, black, glossed with bronzy purple. Immature: Similar to adults but with white tips to many of the black feathers and with narrow black quill streaks on many of the white body feathers.

Range—"Breeds locally from northern Minnesota, southern Wisconsin, southern Indiana (formerly Ohio), North Carolina, and South Carolina, to Florida, Alabama, and eastern Mexico. Winters south of the United States. Accidental or casual in New Mexico, Colorado, southern Saskatchewan, southern Manitoba, Michigan, northern Wisconsin, Ontario, New Brunswick, Pennsylvania, New York, Vermont, Massachusetts, and Connecticut; also in England and the Greater Antilles." (A. O. U.) Casual in New Jersey (Stone). It is very evident that the Swallow-tailed Kite has today a much more restricted breeding range than that given above and it no longer breeds in Minnesota (Roberts), Iowa (Du Mont), Indiana (Hadley), North Carolina (Pearson), Alabama (Howell), Oklahoma (Nice), or Texas (Carroll). South Carolina, formerly common, now rare (Sprunt).

A representative race is found in Central and South America.

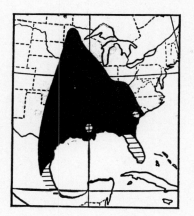

SWALLOW-TAILED KITE
Ruled Area—Breeding Range
Black Area—Former Breeding
Range

MISSISSIPPI KITE

Ictinia misisippiensis (Wilson)

Other Names. Louisiana Kite, Blue Kite, Mosquito Hawk, Pigeon Hawk.

The Mississippi Kite is another of the potentially beneficial species which is too rare to have any present economic importance but which has considerable esthetic

MISSISSIPPI KITE
Adults

and scientific value. *It should be given complete protection at all times.* A campaign of education is needed if the species is to be saved from early extermination, for it is today found in but few localities.

The Mississippi Kite is a long-winged and graceful but rather dull-colored bird, sometimes seen sailing in easy circles at a great height, at other times sweeping along like a huge Swallow over the forests or low along wooded waterways. Its general bluish tone, with lighter almost white head, darker wings and black fan-shaped tail, easily distinguish it in flight. When perched, the grayish secondaries form a lighter bar across the dark gray of the closed wings and the chestnut inner webs of the primaries are not visible. Dr. Witmer Stone (1924) describes its "peculiar habit of tilting up so that the entire upper surface was brought into view" when in flight and which "brought into prominence the jet black square cut tail—the pale gray head, which appeared almost white as the sunlight struck it, was also conspicuous and the bicolored wings, the anterior portion of which was dark slate and the posterior border (exposed primaries) pale gray, in strong contrast." No other Hawk resembles this species in proportions and coloration.

FEEDING HABITS

The food of the Mississippi Kite is similar to that of the Swallow-tailed Kite; like the latter bird it frequently carries its prey in its talons and eats it while in flight. Alexander Wilson (1832), who first described this species, saw the birds catching cicadas in Mississippi. Thomas Nuttall (1832) says it feeds upon insects, "probably small birds," lizards, snakes, and other reptiles. J. J. Audubon (1840-1844) says "it never attacks poultry." Henry Nehrling (1882) says it eats cotton worms, small snakes, and lizards. A. K. Fisher (1893) states that it eats "insects, such as the larger beetles, grasshoppers and locusts, lizards, small snakes, and frogs. It has never been known to molest birds or animals." A. F. Ganier (1902) says cicadas or locusts form a large part of its food in Mississippi. A .T. Wayne (1910) says it feeds almost entirely on insects and lizards. G. W. Stephens in a letter to A. C. Bent (*mss.*, 1933) wrote that it feeds largely on locusts and cicadas but adds that he has found the remains of toads, mice, and young rabbits in the nests with young.

RESULTS OF EXAMINATIONS OF STOMACHS AND CROPS

Authority	Number Examined	Mammals	Poultry or Game	Other Birds	Other Vertebrates	Insects	Miscellaneous	Empty
Wilson, Alex., 1832	3	0	0	0	0	3	0	0
Coues, Elliott, 1883	1	0	0	0	0	1	0	0
Singley, J. A., 1888	1	0	0	0	0	1	0	0
Fisher, A. K., 1893	4	0	0	0	0	4	0	0
Ganier, A. F., 1902	1	0	0	0	0	1	0	0
Wetmore, Alex., 1909 . . .	3	0	0	0	0	3	0	0
Bur. Biol. Surv., 1893-1931 .	15	0	0	0	0	15	0	0
Totals	28	0	0	0	0	28	0	0

EVERGLADE KITE

Adult male in foreground, adult female in flight, young male on ground

Description—Length about 13 to 17 inches, spread about 34.5 to 37 inches. Adult: General color bluish gray, much darker than in White-tailed Kite; somewhat lighter on head, neck, and secondary flight feathers, darker on shoulders and primaries; primaries have part of inner webs chestnut, tail black, square-ended or slightly notched; eyes red; legs vermillion or orange. Immature: Above more or less streaked with black and white; below spotted with reddish brown and buffy; tail and wing quills black tipped with white.

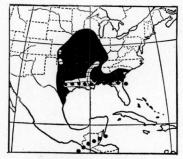

MISSISSIPPI KITE
Ruled Area—Breeding Range
Black Area—Former Breeding Range
Dotted Lines—Boundaries of
Winter Range

Range—"Lower Austral Zone (chiefly); breeds from northeastern Kansas, southern Illinois, southern Indiana, and South Carolina south to Texas and Florida. Winters in Florida and southern Texas south rarely to Guatemala. Casual in Iowa; accidental in Colorado, Nebraska, Wisconsin, New Jersey, and Pennsylvania." (A. O. U.) No longer breeding except in parts of South Carolina, Kansas, Oklahoma, Tennessee and the Gulf States.

EVERGLADE KITE
Rostrhamus sociabilis plumbeus (RIDGWAY)

Other Names. Snail Hawk, Hook-bill Hawk, Black Hawk, Black Kite, Sociable Marsh Hawk.

The highly specialized Everglade Kite is found in the United States only in the vicinity of extensive fresh water marshes in a restricted portion of the Florida peninsula where it feeds exclusively, so far as known, upon large snails of the genus *Ampullaria*. As drainage projects dry up these marsh areas, the habitat of this interesting bird becomes more and more restricted and there is real danger that this distinctive species is due to disappear before many years as a breeding bird in the United States unless active steps can be taken to preserve it. As the snails upon which it feeds have no known value to man, the Everglade Kite has no economic claim for consideration, but it is a very interesting example of special adaptations for a limited niche in our avian fauna. *It should be given complete protection at all times.*

The silhouette of the Everglade Kite is very different from that of any of the other Kites, its broad wings being much more suggestive of the buteonine Hawks or true "Buzzards." Its flight somewhat suggests that of the Marsh Hawk, and both birds show similar deliberation when hunting their prey, but the flight of the Kite is more labored than that of the Harrier and it progresses with more flappings of the long but proportionately wider wings. Both species show considerable white near the base of the tail, but that of the Harrier is higher up, on the tail coverts and rump, while that of the Kite is largely on the tail feathers themselves. The male

Harrier is much lighter colored than the male Kite but the females and young are more nearly alike in color. The Kite is singularly slow when soaring, according to W. H. Hudson, who adds that its expanded tail "is all the time twisted about in the most singular manner, moved from side to side, and turned up until its edge is nearly at a right angle with the plane of its body." Allan Brooks describes it as hovering "in a peculiar sort of way, the wings flexed at the carpal joint." The bright orange or vermillion feet are conspicuous at some distance.

FEEDING HABITS

All observers are agreed that the Everglade Kite feeds exclusively upon snails of the genus *Ampullaria*, which are extracted from the shell by means of the long, slender and strongly hooked bill, but the exact method used is difficult to detect. Herbert Lang (1924) describes his observations in Georgetown, British Guiana, at some length. The snails remain in the water during the hotter part of the day but in the early morning and late afternoon are found at the surface or creeping about on the marsh vegetation. The Kite quarters back and forth low over the water, suggesting a sea gull at a distance. Often it hovers over one spot for a considerable interval, then dives down to pick up a snail which it carries in its talons to some favorite perching place in a bush or low tree. Here it stands for several seconds motionless, on one leg, holding the snail in the long claws of the other foot. Soon the snail, which had withdrawn into its shell when picked up, closing tightly its operculum, begins slowly to extrude its slimy body. Suddenly, like a flash, the Kite grasps the body of the snail, between the operculum and the shell, in its blunt-edged but deeply hooked bill. The muscular contraction of the snail's body apparently detaches it from its attachment within the shell, and a moment later, with a shake of the Kite's head, the shell is tossed aside and the body swallowed, including the operculum. A. H. Howell (1932) says the snail is swallowed "in pieces about a half or three-quarters of an inch in length" after having been "extracted" with the bill. Favorite eating places are marked with considerable accumulations of empty snail shells.

EVERGLADE KITE
Ruled Area—Breeding Range

Description—Length 16 to 18 inches, spread about 45 inches. The slender, over-developed and noticeably hooked beak is black, the cere, naked lores, feet and rather long legs are vermillion, orange, or yellow, and the wings are broader proportionately than those of the other Kites, giving it a very different appearance. Adult male: Uniform dark slaty blue, almost black, except head and upper back which are lighter gray, and tail coverts, basal half of outer tail feathers, and narrow tips of all tail feathers, which are white. Adult female: Upper parts rusty blackish; under parts streaked and mottled with brownish and buffy or whitish; the dark part of the tail is browner and the white tip wider; there is some white on the sides of the head. Immature: A brighter more chestnut shade of brown much variegated with darker brown, yellowish and white; tail as in adults.

According to Bent and Friedmann, apparently two or more years are required for this species to attain fully adult plumage, as it is known to breed in intermediate stages of plumage.

Range—"Peninsular Florida, Cuba, eastern Mexico, and Central America. Winters from central Florida southward." (A. O. U.)

A representative race is found in South America.

AMERICAN GOSHAWK

Adult at left, immature at right

THE ACCIPITERS OR BIRD HAWKS

This group is represented by three species in North America, all characterized by proportionately short, round-ended wings and long tails, which give them a typical "accipitrine" silhouette. When perched, the closed wings reach only to about the upper third of the tail. When flying, the length of the bird is nearly three-fifths of its expanse. Accipiters are less robust appearing than typical Buteos, the other Hawks with round-ended wings, and their manner of flight is different, consisting, when in open country, of a few powerful wing strokes alternating with brief periods of straightforward sailing or gliding, at which latter times the long tails of the Accipiters are very evident. When pursuing their prey, which is very largely composed of birds, they dart through the trees and thickets with great speed and with amazing skill in avoiding obstacles and following the evolutions of their panic stricken quarry. When they perch, it is often within the branches of a tree where they are hidden from view.

AMERICAN GOSHAWKS
Astur atricapillus (Wilson)

Other Names. Blue Darter, Blue Hawk, Blue Partridge Hawk, Blue Hen Hawk, Hen Hawk, Chicken Hawk, Dove Hawk.

Until we ourselves are ready to become vegetarians and to stop all eating of meat, it is hardly fitting for us to brand the Goshawk "murderer" and "blood-thirsty wretch," favorite epithets of the sentimentalist and the gunner alike, merely because the Goshawk obeys its natural instincts in seeking out its food. At times the Goshawk may become very persistent and destructive about poultry farms and game rearing establishments, under which conditions control measures may be necessary. On the other hand, it doubtless performs a very definite and valuable service in weeding out the slow moving, weakened or diseased individuals which otherwise might spread contagion or devitalize the stock of our wild game birds or mammals. In Nova Scotia and New Brunswick, where the Goshawk is a summer resident, the Ruffed Grouse flourishes wherever it is not overshot, despite the presence of this predator. The Goshawk also kills many rabbits which are well known to be among the enemies of the fruit grower and forester, and it is one of our best natural controls upon the red squirrel. It is northern in distribution and seldom appears in the United States in sufficient numbers to be a very important economic factor.

The Goshawk is power, speed and wildness combined in the form of one of nature's most fearless creatures. It frequents wilderness regions except when driven into civilization by hunger and retreats rapidly from settled areas. It is nowhere common, except in migration during limited periods of the year. It is frequently misidentified in the field and other Hawks are confused with it, as the figures of the Pennsylvania Game Commission indicate, where, of 503 birds shot to obtain the state bounty, only 76 were Goshawks.

The Goshawk is the largest and most robust appearing of our accipitrine Hawks, which are characterized by their short round-ended wings and long tails. It breeds principally in Canada and in its winter visits to the United States it is often surprisingly daring, taking its toll of poultry almost out of the hands of the surprised farmer and picking up game in front of the very guns of the sportsmen. Often it perches in a tree on the edge of the woods, waiting its chance from the concealment of the branches, and then like a winged arrow darts upon its unsuspecting victim, carrying away chickens of nearly its own weight with hardly any checking of its impetuous flight. At other times it hunts low over the thickets, flying rapidly with brief alternations of flapping and sailing. In straight flight the wing beats are powerful and rapid, strongly suggesting a Duck Hawk or Gyrfalcon. At such times, however, the long tail and blunt wings are apparent. The wings and tail are relatively a little longer than those of the Cooper's Hawk, though the wings are not as long as those of one of the buteonine Hawks, while the tail is longer than in the Buteos.

Though usually silent except when its nesting area is invaded, it sometimes utters a series of loud staccato cries, *kak kak kak*, repeated many times, or a *kwee-kwee-kwee* "with a tinge of harshness impossible to indicate in words."

Immatures of this group are extremely difficult to distinguish from each other except by size, and seasonal occurrence. In much of its range in the United States the Goshawk is present only in winter, when the Cooper's Hawk is usually rare or absent. The adult Eastern Goshawk is very evenly light gray below and dark gray above, with no very definite marks except the whitish eyebrow and the blackish crown and ear-stripe. The Western Goshawk is a considerably darker bird. The adult Goshawk is grayer and more uniform in color tone than any other northern Hawk except the male Marsh Hawk and the very rare Gyrfalcons. The barring of the under surface of the wings is very regular and there is no suggestion of the "wrist-mark" seen in many of the buteonine Hawks. The latter group are distinguished by their short tails and heavy appearing bodies. The only other Hawks which approach the Goshawk in size and color are the Gyrfalcons but the latter have longer, narrower, more pointed wings and are adapted for hunting in the open, killing their prey in full flight, while the accipitrine Hawks are adapted for quick turning and dodging among the branches and undergrowth of the forest. The accipitrine Hawks, after striking their prey, usually fly with it in their talons to a perch within the cover of a tree, where they may devour it unobserved.

FEEDING HABITS

The Goshawk, wherever found and of whatever race, is one of the very few of our Hawks that feeds principally on birds, as is shown by field studies and stomach examinations. Under some conditions it eats many mammals. J. J. Audubon (1840–1844) lists among its avian prey Mallards, Teals, Black Ducks, Ruffed Grouse, Canada Grouse, Passenger Pigeons, Grackles, and domestic fowls and ducks. L. M. Turner (1886) states that lemmings form a considerable part of its food in Alaska but that it also eats many Ptarmigan. H. E. Woods and A. A. Cross (*in litt.*, 1931) examined a nest in Massachusetts and on three visits found 12 chipmunks, 1 red squirrel, 2 young Ruffed Grouse, and a Crow. O. L. Austin, Jr. (1932), says that their food in Labrador consists in the main of hares, Ptarmigan and mice. A. C. Bent (*mss.*, 1933) lists in the food of the Goshawk rabbits, hares, squirrels, chipmunks, weasels, lemmings, mice, Murres, Teals and other wild Ducks, Snipe, poultry, Quail, Grouse, Ptarmigan, Pheasants, Pigeons, Doves, Crows, Kingfishers, Grackles, Blackbirds, a few Sparrows, locusts, larvae of moths, and beetles.

RESULTS OF EXAMINATIONS OF STOMACHS AND CROPS

Authority	Number Examined	Mammals	Poultry or Game	Other Birds	Other Vertebrates	Insects	Miscellaneous	Empty
Fisher, A. K., 1893	28	10	9	2	0	3	1	8
Deane, Ruthven, 1907 . . .	48	0	33	0	0	0	4	11
Bailey, B. H., 1918	8	1	0	1	0	0	0	6
Brewster, Wm., 1925	1	1	0	0	0	0	0	0
Sutton, G. M., 1927	251	89	120	27	2	0	1	49
Gross, A. O., 1928	258	37	110	3	0	0	2	104
Munro, J. A., 1929	6	1	3	2	0	0	0	0
Miller, W. DeW., *mss.*, 1929	30	10	11	1	0	0	0	8
Luttringer, L. A., Jr., 1930 .	25	9	15	1	0	0	0	?
Smith, J. D., *in litt.* 1930 . .	5	1	1	0	0	0	0	3
Brooks, Allan, *in litt.*, 1931 .	1	1	0	0	0	0	0	0
Sutton, G. M., 1931	205	72	140	11	0	0	0	?
Snyder, L. L., 1932	15	1	5	1	0	0	0	9
Totals	881	233	447	49	2	3	8	168

There are two geographical races of this species in North America, the Eastern and the Western Goshawk.

EASTERN GOSHAWK
Astur atricapillus atricapillus (WILSON)

Description—Length of male 20 to 22 inches, spread 40 to 44.5 inches; length of female 22 to 26.5 inches, spread 44 to 47 inches. Adult: Above dark bluish slaty, becoming blackish on crown, and whitish on nape of neck; a whitish streak over eye and a blackish stripe through eye

SHARP-SHINNED HAWK
Adult at right, immature at left

and over ear region, are diagnostic marks; flight feathers blackish with about six gray bars; under parts white or pale gray, finely barred with black or dark gray pencillings and narrow black shaft streaks, except under tail coverts which are unmarked; tail bluish gray narrowly tipped with white and crossed with about four dusky bands; iris red; legs and feet yellow. Immature: But for its larger size the young Goshawk is very much like the immature Cooper's Hawk but it has a noticeable light superciliary streak or "eyebrow."

Range—"Breeds in the Boreal zones from northwestern Alaska, northwestern Mackenzie, northern Manitoba, southeastern Ontario, northern Quebec (Ungava), and New-

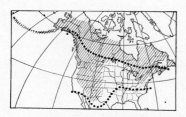

AMERICAN GOSHAWKS
Ruled Area—Breeding Range
Dotted Lines—Boundaries of
Winter Range

foundland south to interior British Columbia, Michigan, northern New York, northern New England, Massachusetts (casually), and in the mountains to Pennsylvania and western Maryland. Winters from Alaska and the southern Canadian provinces to southern California, northern Mexico, Texas, Oklahoma, Missouri, Kentucky, Illinois, Indiana, northern Ohio, West Virginia, and Virginia; migrations periodic and irregular. Casual or accidental in Idaho, Arizona and Florida; also in Ireland." (A. O. U.)

WESTERN GOSHAWK
Astur atricapillus striatulus RIDGWAY

Description—Adult: Above dark plumbeous, darkest on crown; below very finely and closely barred and pencilled with black, appearing nearly uniform bluish gray. Immature: Brownish black above; below whitish with broad black streaks and spots.

Range—"Breeds in Boreal zones of the Pacific coast region from Cook Inlet, Alaska, possibly south to California in the central Sierra Nevada (Yosemite National Park), Arizona, New Mexico, and Chihuahua. Winters through much of its breeding range and south to southern California (vicinity of San Diego) and northern Mexico." (A. O. U.)

SHARP-SHINNED HAWK
Accipiter velox velox (WILSON)

Other Names. Sharp-shin, Little Blue Darter, Bullet Hawk, Slate-colored Hawk, Bird Hawk, Sparrow Hawk, Pigeon Hawk, Partridge Hawk, Chicken Hawk, Fowl Hawk.

The little Sharp-shinned Hawk is one of the most persecuted of our Hawks, due to its habit of feeding upon small birds. Its small size prevents its doing any great damage to adult game birds or poultry, but for a short period of the nesting season it may be destructive to young Pheasants, young chickens and the like, where such food is easily obtainable. Generally game breeders can keep young birds under wire until they can shift for themselves. During migration Sharp-shinned Hawks frequently become abundant at points like Cape May, N. J., or Point Pelee, Ontario, where birds which bred over hundreds of square miles are concentrated for a few weeks of the year, particularly during September and October. At this time the number of small birds taken is quite considerable, but by and large, as a nesting bird, the Sharp-shinned Hawk is decreasing, especially in the East and Northeast, Massachusetts, New Jersey and the more settled areas. In most of its breeding localities, the proportion of Sharp-shinned Hawks to the total Passerine population is so small (at Wyanokie, New Jersey, over a period of 19 years ten pairs of Sharp-shinned Hawks were found as compared with a total of 31,436 pairs, chiefly land birds) that its importance as a destructive agent in the past has been over-emphasized. While it does not need special protection except at certain points of concentration during migration, and while it may even require control in some sanctuaries or under certain conditions, it is one of nature's checks against over-production and is of value in removing diseased or weakened individuals among our smaller bird species. It is unquestionably decreasing, as indicated above, but still remains fairly common in the northern forested regions.

The flight of the Sharp-shin is rapid and direct; it is not often seen to circle or soar, and it never poises and hovers with rapidly beating wings as is characteristic of the smaller Falcons. It is often observed dashing into a thicket in headlong pursuit of its feathered prey while consternation reigns among the Songbirds. It seldom utters any notes except in the breeding season; when about its nest it sometimes emits "a high *kee ki ki ki* or a thin whining *whee whee*"; it has also cackling notes suggestive of the Belted Kingfisher, "flicker-like alarm notes" or a series of short rather shrill screams.

The Cooper's Hawk very closely resembles the Sharp-shin though averaging larger, but it has a rounded end to its tail and the crown of the head, in adults, is decidedly darker than the rest of the upper parts. The Pigeon Hawk is the only other Hawk which resembles the Sharp-shin in both size and general coloration, but the adult Sharp-shin is finely barred below with brown while the Pigeon Hawk is heavily streaked, and a glimpse of the latter's long, pointed wings makes differentiation easy. When perched, the folded wings of the Sharp-shin reach only to the upper third or the middle of its tail, while those of the Pigeon Hawk reach nearly to the tip of its tail. The bright chestnut and bluish colors of the slightly smaller American Sparrow Hawk will quickly identify this species, and it has the slender pointed wings of the typical Falcon.

FEEDING HABITS

The little Sharp-shinned Hawk unquestionably feeds principally on small birds, only rarely eating mammals or any other creatures except birds. J. J. Audubon (1831–1839) says its food "consists chiefly of birds of various sizes, from the smallest of our warblers to the Passenger Pigeon and young chickens—it feeds occasionally on small reptiles and insects," and he shot one which had just captured a shrew. A. K. Fisher (1893) says that its food "is made up almost entirely of wild birds and young poultry, though occasionally it will take a few insects, mice, reptiles or batrachians." Paul Bartsch (1897) reports finding remains of many Songbirds about a nest in Iowa "as well as some bones belonging to small rodents, spermophiles perhaps." E. H. Forbush (1927) states that the stomach of a Massachusetts bird held 52 grasshoppers, many other insects, and a mouse. R. O. Morris (1892) reports seeing a Sharp-shin fasten to a Wood Duck, and C. J. Maynard (1881) saw one strike a full-grown Black-crowned Night Heron; two unusual examples which give an idea of the courage and impetuosity of this little Raptor, A. C. Bent (mss., 1933) says that while its bill of fare includes a few mice, shrews, frogs, lizards, locusts, grasshoppers, crickets, large moths, butterflies and beetles, its principal food is birds, and he lists among its victims Sandpipers, Woodpeckers, Swifts, Flycatchers, Horned Larks, Cowbirds, Orioles, Blackbirds, Grackles, Jays, Meadowlarks, many Sparrows, Towhees, Vireos, many Warblers, Mockingbirds, Thrashers, Catbirds, Wrens, Nuthatches, Chickadees, Creepers, Kinglets, Robins, Thrushes and Bluebirds.

RESULTS OF EXAMINATIONS OF STOMACHS AND CROPS

Authority	Number Examined	Mammals	Poultry or Game	Other Birds	Other Vertebrates	Insects	Miscellaneous	Empty
Warren, B. H., 1890	19	2	8	9	0	2	0	0
Fisher, A. K., 1893	159	6	6	99	0	5	0	52
Bailey, B. H., 1918	13	1	0	9	0	0	0	3
Ferguson, A. L. & H. L., 1922	483	16	?	530	0	38	0	?
Sutton, G. M., 1928	113	0	?	62	0	0	0	51
Munro, J. A., 1929	6	0	2	4	0	0	0	0
Miller, W. DeW., mss., 1929	206	1	0	185	0	0	0	?
Luttringer, L. A., Jr. 1930 .	?	1	0	10	0	0	0	0
Snyder, L. L., in litt., 1931 . .	31	1	0	36	0	0	0	0
Totals	1030+	28	16+	844	0	45	0	106+

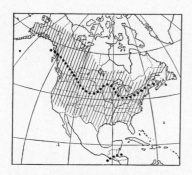

SHARP-SHINNED HAWK
Ruled Area—Breeding Range
Dotted Lines—Boundaries of
Winter Range

Description—The Sharp-shinned Hawk is our smallest accipitrine Hawk, usually distinguished by its square or slightly notched tail from the very similar Cooper's Hawk, though this is not an infallible mark. The sexes are alike in coloration but vary greatly in size, the female being sometimes a quarter longer and nearly twice the bulk of the male. Length of male 10 to 12 inches, spread 20 to 23 inches; length of female 12 to 14 inches, spread 24 to 27 inches. Adult: Upper parts dark bluish gray; under parts whitish, heavily cross-barred with reddish brown, except throat which is finely streaked, and under tail coverts which are unmarked white; wings finely and evenly barred, noticeable in flight; square or slightly notched tail barred

COOPER'S HAWK

Adult perched, immature in flight

with three or four rather narrow bands of blackish brown above and grayish white below. Immature: Upper parts brownish; under parts whitish streaked with brown or black.

Range—"Breeds nearly throughout the United States and Canada from northwestern Alaska, Mackenzie (Great Bear Lake), northern Manitoba, northern Ontario, central Quebec, southern Labrador, and Newfoundland south to northern Florida, the Gulf coast, Texas, Arizona, and west-central California. Winters from southeastern Alaska, southern British Columbia, western Montana, southern Minnesota (casually), northern Nebraska, Indiana, Illinois, Ohio, New York, southern Vermont, southern New Hampshire, and New Brunswick (casually), to Guatemala, and (casually) Panama. Accidental in the Bahamas." (A. O. U.) Occasional in Bermuda (Bradlee).

Three other races of *Accipiter velox* are recognized from the West Indies.

COOPER'S HAWK
Accipiter cooperi (BONAPARTE)

Other Names. Big Blue Darter, Bullet Hawk, Swift Hawk, Black-capped Hawk, Privateer, Striker, Chicken Hawk, Hen Hawk, Quail Hawk, Partridge Hawk, Pigeon Hawk, Pheasant Hawk, Long-tailed Chicken Hawk.

The Cooper's Hawk, when common, may be extremely destructive to small birds, young poultry, and game birds. H. L. Stoddard (1931) says that "these destructive Hawks probably harvest a crop of Quail in the aggregate, during the course of their 365-day open season, comparable with that taken by sportsmen in their much shorter time afield" in the heavily populated Quail preserves of the South. The manner of hunting employed by the Cooper's Hawk, a sudden on-slaught from sheltering woodlands, makes it difficult to control about poultry and game farms, and it is seldom captured by the use of pole traps, which are, on the other hand, often very fatal to many of our beneficial species of Hawks as well as to other birds. The Cooper's Hawk is one of the commonest species in many localities, where the "Mouse Hawks" and "Grasshopper Hawks" have almost disappeared under human persecution. All three of the accipitrine Hawks are today sufficiently common so that we have no immediate fear of their extinction, but unless the tremendous shooting on their lines of flight is curtailed they may soon become quite rare.

About poultry and game farms, at certain seasons of the year, the Sharp-shinned Hawk and the Cooper's Hawk may occasionally call for control by properly authorized persons in order to reduce their destructiveness to unprotected game.

Poultry killing by Hawks is frequently much exaggerated, and the shot-gun as a remedy should be called upon only when the predator is actually causing damage.

Much that has been written about the Sharp-shin applies equally to the Cooper's Hawk, with due allowances for the larger size of the latter bird. Their manner of hunting is very similar, though the Cooper's Hawk may indulge in more circling and soaring than the Sharp-shin and J. T. Nichols says, "there is a subtle difference in the character of the flight between the two, that of the Sharp-shin giving the effect of buoyancy and the Cooper's of momentum." The Cooper's Hawk is likely to be more noisy than the Sharp-shin, its notes including a rather harsh *kluk, kluk, kluk,* a far-reaching *swee-ew* or *psee-ur,* and a shrill *quick, quick, quick,* repeated many times in rapid succession. About its nest "its metallic *tick, tick, tick* makes identification easy."

Young Cooper's Hawks are very much like young Goshawks in color, but even large females average a little smaller than small male Goshawks and they lack the pale superciliary line or "eyebrow" of the immature Goshawk. The under surface of the wings of all the accipitrine Hawks is regularly barred to the tips of the flight feathers, a characteristic lacking in the Broad-winged Hawk which is often found in similar wooded areas and which is about the same length as the Cooper's Hawk but with considerably longer wings. The Pigeon Hawk has barred wings but they are long, narrow and pointed instead of broad and rounded.

FEEDING HABITS

The Cooper's Hawk is a confirmed bird eater like the Sharp-shinned Hawk, its larger size making it more destructive to poultry and game birds however. Elliott Coues (1874) says it "destroys hares, grouse, teal, and even the young of larger ducks—besides capturing the usual variety of smaller birds and quadrupeds" and occasional reptiles and insects. A. K. Fisher (1893) summarizes its food as almost entirely wild birds and poultry with occasional small mammals, reptiles, batrachians, and insects. F. C. Pellett (1912) studied food brought to a nest: during the

RESULTS OF EXAMINATIONS OF STOMACHS AND CROPS

Authority	Number Examined	Mammals	Poultry or Game	Other Birds	Other Vertebrates	Insects	Miscellaneous	Empty
Warren, B. H., 1890	34	5	18	10	1	3	0	?
Fisher, A. K., 1893	133	11	34	52	4	2	0	39
Bailey, B. H., 1918	8	1	0	7	0	0	0	1
Sutton, G. M., 1928	11	1	1	5	0	0	0	4
Munro, J. A., 1929	6	1	3	2	0	0	0	0
Miller, W. deW., mss., 1929	47	15	6	11	1	0	0	16
Luttringer, L. A., Jr., 1930 .	36	16	7	2	0	0	10	0
Stoddard, H. L., 1931 . . .	9	0	3	5	0	0	0	0
Snyder, L. L., 1932	20	1	3	9	0	0	0	7
Pearson, T. G., 1933-b . . .	118	14	3	43	0	0	0	62
Totals	422	65	78	146	6	5	10	129

first weeks only poultry, pigeons and small birds were found; later, many spermophiles and chickens were fed to the young. A. R. Smith (1915) says that as the mountain streams in Arkansas dry, the Cooper's Hawk eats minnows. Grinnell and Storer (1924) found a chipmunk and eight species of birds under a nest in

California. William Brewster (1925) wrote of Cooper's Hawk "its victims are almost exclusively birds, varying in size from a Robin to that of a half-grown Ruffed Grouse." E. H. Forbush (1927) adds to its feathered prey "snakes and other reptiles, or even mice, grasshoppers and crickets." P. L. Errington (*in litt.*, 1930) reports that food material recovered from nests and from the gullets of nestlings in Wisconsin included remains of three rodents; poultry or game birds, two; other birds, fourteen. T. G. Pearson (*in litt.*, 1930) writes that one of the wardens of the National Association of Audubon Societies in Florida saw a Cooper's Hawk bring down an adult Little Blue Heron. Dr. Pearson also reports (1933-a) that thirty birds and one insect were found in twenty-two stomachs from New Jersey.

Description—A larger edition of the Sharp-shinned Hawk, differing principally in having a rounded end to the tail. Length of male 14 to 18 inches, spread 27 to 30 inches; length of female 16.5 to 20 inches, spread 29 to 36 inches. Adults have top of head blackish and upper parts are likely to be a clearer and more uniform bluish than is the case with the Sharp-shin. Immatures are practically indistinguishable from immature Sharp-shins except for size and the rounded tail.

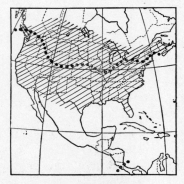

COOPER'S HAWK
Ruled Area—Breeding Range
Dotted Lines—Boundaries of
Winter Range

Range—"Breeds from southern British Columbia, central Alberta, southern Ontario, southern Quebec, and Prince Edward Island to the southern border of the United States and northern Mexico. Winters from southwestern British Columbia, Washington, California, Colorado, Nebraska, southern Illinois, Indiana, Ohio, southern Michigan (rarely), southern Ontario (rarely), southern New York, Massachusetts, and southern Maine to Costa Rica" (A. O. U.).

RED-TAILED HAWK
Adults at left, immatures at right

THE BUTEONINE OR BUZZARD HAWKS

The buteonine Hawks are heavy, sluggish appearing Hawks, characterized by fairly long round-ended wings, short tails, and robust bodies. Their manner of hunting is characteristic also, either by perching in some commanding position where they may patiently watch for their victims, or leisurely sailing for long periods of time in great circles with set and almost motionless pinions and open fan-shaped tail. These birds are generally excellent friends of the farmer, living very largely upon mice and other harmful rodents, though occasional individuals may "fall from grace" and become destroyers of poultry. In England a close relative of our Red-tailed Hawk is known as the "Common Buzzard"; it is indeed most unfortunate that our early English settlers in this country failed to transfer the name "Buzzard" to our Hawks of the genus *Buteo* but instead gave it to the Vultures of our southern States.

RED-TAILED HAWKS
Buteo borealis (GMELIN)

Other Names. Red-tail, Red-tailed Buzzard, Red Hawk, Hen Hawk, Big Hen Hawk, Chicken Hawk, White-breasted Chicken Hawk, Squealing Hawk, Buzzard Hawk.

The Red-tailed Hawk, wherever found and regardless of color, is ordinarily a decidedly beneficial species, its food consisting very largely of mice, ground squirrels or other injurious rodents, varied occasionally with small birds, snakes, frogs, and insects. Certain individuals, finding young chickens on open runways an easy prey, may develop bad habits and justify the farmer in killing them, but this trait is not common, in spite of the widely prevailing prejudice against them, and the harm done by these individuals is far outweighed by the good done by the species as a whole. Because of these erring individuals, however, the Red-tail is misnamed "Hen Hawk" and is sentenced to death without a fair trial. It is too heavy and sluggish in its movements to capture many of our small Songbirds or healthy game birds. In consideration of its efficiency as a rodent destroyer, *it should be given protection* and an active campaign of education should be waged in its favor. It is one of the species which has diminished markedly in recent years over much of its range.

The Red-tailed Hawk is essentially a soaring Hawk. It is most often seen (and often heard) sailing high overhead, wheeling in great spirals with wings and tail widely spread, changing its course by merely tilting its tail sideways, and maintaining its lofty elevation with only an occasional stroke of its broad wings. At other times it perches for hours at a time in some commanding situation, usually a dead tree or, in mountainous regions, a ledge. When startled it gets up quickly and with heavy sweeps of its broad pinions rapidly gains momentum and then glides or sails in a spiral course which soon carries it, without apparent change in the relative positions of wings and tail, to a high altitude. It is a noisy bird, especially in the spring of the year. Its common call is a shrill long-drawn-out whistle or wheezy scream or squeal, with a sputtering quality which suggests escaping steam; it is sometimes written *kee-aahr-r-r* or *quee-oo*. It is higher pitched and longer than the well-known "Blue Jay note" of the Red-shouldered Hawk.

The Red-tail is one of the largest of the true Buteos, after the two Rough-legged Hawks. It soars in the widest circles and with the least flapping of the wings. If watched throughout a complete circle the reddish upper surface of the tail of the adult will usually appear for at least a brief glimpse or will show from below when the light shines through, and this is of course diagnostic. Seen from below the wings are largely whitish, often with a noticeable "wrist-mark" (a dark blotch near the bend of the wing in front), and with dark tips to the flight feathers; they never show the dark and light barring of the Red-shoulder. The primaries are separated and bend upwards slightly at the tips when the bird is soaring. The throat and a large area on the lower breast, in typical specimens, are nearly white, separated by a more or less complete pectoral band (never as solid as in Swainson's Hawk, however), and there is a second, more broken band, across the abdomen. There are all stages from this typical light phase to birds which are almost wholly sooty brown below. The Western Red-tail especially is noted for the wide variation in its colors.

Young Red-tails usually lack the "wrist-mark" and the dark tips of the flight feathers are less marked than in the adult. They are very much like young Red-shoulders and can be distinguished in the field only with difficulty; the streaking of the under parts of the Red-shoulder is usually quite uniformly distributed while that of the Red-tail shows more or less of the zoning of the adult. Some rusty color usually shows on the shoulders of the Red-shoulder at all ages and the bird is slightly smaller and less robust appearing than the Red-tail. Dr. G. M. Sutton says that "the flight of the Red-shoulder is noticeably more rapid, buoyant and owl-like than that of the Red-tailed Hawk," and J. T. Nichols remarks that the Red-tail "seems to have a more ponderous, less gliding character" to its flight than the Red-shoulder. In Swainson's Hawk in typical light plumage, the broken abdominal band of the Red-tail is lacking and the abdomen is the lightest part of the under surface, the pectoral band is broader and more distinct, and the white area on the throat is smaller; the pectoral band may be gray, brown or cinnamon; the wings are slightly narrower and more pointed; the tail is grayish, narrowly barred with darker and is never chestnut or rusty. The American Rough-leg is slightly larger than the Red-tail and in the light phase usually shows contrasting areas of dark and light quite different from any pattern of the Red-tail. The Ferruginous Rough-leg is also larger, is more solidly white below with rufous "pantaloons" and its tail is lighter, whitening decidedly toward its base. The bases of the primaries of both Rough-legs, even in their darkest melanistic phases, show a flash of whitish in flight, which is not present in the dark phases of the Red-tail.

FEEDING HABITS

The Red-tailed Hawk shows a wide range in its feeding habits, with the emphasis upon mammalian food. William Lloyd (1887) says that in western Texas this species feeds upon prairie dogs, cottontails, jack rabbits, and occasionally on Scaled Quail. W. L. Finley (1905) says that when the Columbia River overflowed, a pair of Western Red-tails fed their young on carp and catfish. J. S. Dixon (1906) reports finding gophers, ground squirrels, meadow mice, young cottontails, and two kinds of snakes, at a nest of a Western Red-tail, with ground squirrels predominating. E. S. Cameron (1907) states that a pair in Montana fed their young almost entirely on Western Meadowlarks. F. H. Chittenden (1911) says the Red-tail eats potato bugs at times. F. C. Pellett (1912) found pocket gophers most common at a nest in Iowa but also found gray squirrels, ground squirrels, rats, field mice, and two small chickens. Norman Criddle (1917) examined twenty-eight pellets from Manitoba and found feathers of a Crow and two Vesper Sparrows, with hair of voles, mice, and ground squirrels. J. K. Jensen (1926) reports a medium sized rattlesnake and a large bull snake killed by Red-tails. Verdi Burtch (1927) saw one feeding on a freshly killed Red-shouldered Hawk. E. H. Forbush (1927) found only mice in stomachs he examined in Massachusetts. E. L. Sumner Jr. (1929) found remains of twenty rodents and one snake at a nest of a Western Red-tail. E. D. Naumann (1929) describes one unsuccessfully attacking a large tom-cat. P. G. Redington (1929) records that the Bureau of Biological Survey examined thirty-one stomachs collected in Washington State in 1927: 83% of the contents was ground squirrels, 6% rabbits, 4% meadow mice, and the remainder, about 7%, snakes. A. A. Cross and H. E. Woods (*in litt.*, 1931) found two gray squirrels in one nest, and two red squirrels, three chipmunks and part of a snow-shoe rabbit in another nest in Massachusetts. J. P. Miller (1931) studied five nests of the Western Red-tail and says the food consisted almost entirely of ground squirrels with the exception of one meadow mouse; they averaged six ground squirrels daily for each nest. Townsend Godsey (1931) states that Ernest Schwarz examined a series of stomachs from Missouri and found mice or other rodents in every one; two, however, showed a trace of feathers. T. G. Pearson (1928) quotes W. L. McAtee of the Bureau of Biological Survey on the examination of more than 850 stomachs and crops of Red-tailed Hawks collected in nearly all parts of the United States: only 754 of these held food remains; 654, or more than 86% of these, held mammal remains including 385 mice of different species; 86, or less than 12%, held poultry or game bird remains; 59, or about 8%, other birds; 59, reptiles or batrachians; 106, or 15%, insects. L. L. Snyder (1932) examined

28 stomachs from Ontario: mammals formed 49.8% of the food; poultry and game birds, 11.4%; other birds, 18.5%; reptiles and batrachians, 13.3%; insects, 2.5%; offal, 4.5%.

Often the food of the Red-tail and other buteonine Hawks consists of animals or birds picked up in a dead or crippled condition, which accounts for at least a portion of the poultry or game birds found in their stomachs. It has been a common habit for dead poultry to be used as bait for pole or ground traps about game farms, and it is not correct to assume that *every* bird eaten has been killed by the Hawk itself.

RESULTS OF EXAMINATIONS OF STOMACHS AND CROPS

Authority	Number Examined	Mammals	Poultry or Game	Other Birds	Other Vertebrates	Insects	Miscellaneous	Empty
Warren, B. H., 1890	173	142	17	15	3	3	4	?
Fisher, A. K., 1893	562	409	54	51	97	47	22	89
Arnow, I. T., 1904	1	0	1	0	0	0	0	0
Bailey, B. H., 1918	68	35	10	0	9	21	5	17
Bryant, H. C., 1918	4	4	0	0	0	0	0	0
Miller, Loye, 1920	1	1	0	0	0	0	0	0
Howell, A. H., 1924	1	0	0	0	0	1	0	0
Sutton, G. M., 1928	32	25	1	3	3	4	0	12
Munro, J. A., 1929	6	6	0	0	0	2	0	0
Miller, W. DeW., mss., 1929	45	40	1	3	1	13	0	0
Errington, P. L., in litt., 1930	?	124	11	6	4	0	0	0
Brooks, Allan, in litt., 1931	11	7	0	1	0	1	1	0
Stoddard, H. L., 1931	7	6	0	0	1	0	0	0
Pearson, T. G., 1933-b	102	58	17	6	0	?	8	28
Totals	1013+	857	112	85	118	92	40	146

The A. O. U. Check-List (1931) recognizes five races of *Buteo borealis* in North America, and allied races occur in Jamaica, Haiti, Porto Rico and Costa Rica. J. L. Peters (1932) gives priority of title to the Jamaican race and names eight races of *Buteo jamaicensis*. He places the Eastern Red-tail and the Western Red-tail together under *Buteo jamaicensis borealis*, and assigns to Harlan's Hawk specific rank as *Buteo harlani*. P. A. Taverner (1926) studied a large series of specimens and states that he is "inclined to disregard both *krideri* and *harlani* as separable subspecies and regard them as the dark and light extremes of *calurus* whose distinctive character from *borealis* is greater variability." In the present volume we follow the authority of the Check-List of the American Ornithologists' Union, fourth edition.

EASTERN RED-TAILED HAWK
Buteo borealis borealis (Gmelin)

Description—Length of male 19 to 22.5 inches, spread 46 to 50 inches; length of female 21 to 25 inches, spread 48 to 58 inches. There is considerable variation in color between individuals, especially in the western part of its range, but real melanism is extremely rare or unknown in this subspecies. Adult : Dark chocolate brown above, somewhat mottled with gray or whitish, lighter on head, neck and lower back; tail bright reddish brown with a narrow white tip and usually a black subterminal band; under parts varying from almost white to dirty brown in different individuals, but usually showing a broken band of brownish streaks on the upper breast outlining the white throat and another broader broken band of darker markings across the flanks and upper belly; under surface of flight feathers with black tips; a noticeable "wrist-mark." Immature : Duller brown above and whiter below; dark tips of flight feathers less marked; tail dull brownish or like back, and crossed by six to ten darker bands; banding or "zoning" of under parts less distinct than in adult.

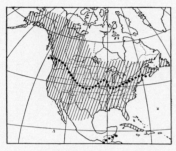

RED-TAILED HAWKS
Ruled Area—Breeding Range
Dotted Lines—Boundaries of
Winter Range

Range—"Breeds from Mackenzie, Saskatchewan, northern Manitoba, northern Ontario, southern Quebec, and Newfoundland south to central southern Texas, northeastern Oklahoma, Arkansas, Alabama, and northern Florida. Winters from Kansas, northeastern Iowa, southern Illinois, Indiana, Ohio, central New York, Vermont, New Hampshire, and southern Maine to northeastern Mexico and the Gulf coast of the United States. Accidental in England." (A. O. U.) Frequent in Bermuda, one former breeding record (Bradlee).

FLORIDA RED-TAILED HAWK
Buteo borealis umbrinus BANGS

Description—Size of Eastern Red-tail. Adult : Darker above than *B. b. borealis;* throat and middle of belly marked with broad conspicuous striping and banding of deep chocolate brown; tail feathers with dark markings (the remains of bands) near the shafts; less diffused reddish below than *B. b. calurus.*

Range—"Southern Florida, Cuba, and the Isle of Pines." (A. O. U.)

KRIDER'S HAWK
Buteo borealis krideri HOOPES
Other Names. Pale Red-tail, Krider's Red-tailed Hawk.

Description—This subspecies is very similar to *B. b. borealis* but is paler and has more white in its plumage; viewed in the field it is noticeably whiter, with a lack of dark markings below and an almost white head. Adult : Upper parts grayish brown with considerable whitish; under parts entirely white or pale buffy or but slightly streaked with brownish and abdominal band sometimes absent; head almost entirely white in some individuals, conspicuous as a field mark; tail pale, light chestnut above and usually lacking the dark subterminal band. Immature : Tail pale rufous or whitish washed with rufous, and crossed with about ten blackish or dark brown bands, and with a white tip.

Range—"Breeds from southern Alberta, southern Saskatchewan, southern Manitoba,

RED-SHOULDERED HAWK

Adults at left and in flight, immature at right

Wyoming, North Dakota and Minnesota south to Nebraska and Missouri. Winters south to Wisconsin, Illinois, Louisiana, and Mississippi. Accidental in Florida and Georgia." (A. O. U.)

WESTERN RED-TAILED HAWK
Buteo borealis calurus CASSIN
Other Names. Black Red-tail, Black Hawk.

Description—This race shows more variation in color than *B. b. borealis* but its chief distinguishing points are more black and rufous on the under parts, especially across the breast, more or less dark barring of the red tail of the adult and more or less red mixed with the dark tail of the immature bird. Melanism is very common and in an extreme case the entire plumage may be an almost uniform sooty brown except for the rufous and dark barred tail.

Range—"Breeds from southeastern Alaska and central western Mackenzie south to southern Lower California and east to the edge of the Great Plains. Winters from southwestern British Columbia and throughout California to Guatemala. Casual farther east in migration." (A. O. U.)

HARLAN'S HAWK
Buteo borealis harlani (AUDUBON)
Other Names. Harlan's Red-tail, Harlan's Buzzard, Black Warrior.

Description—This is another subspecies which shows much variation in individuals. The principal and most constant distinguishing point is the tail, which is usually closely and irregularly mottled with black, brownish, and white; the upper parts may be grayer than *B. b. borealis* or a nearly uniform blackish; the under parts vary from white more or less spotted with black or dusky to sooty brown or nearly black. Immature birds have the tail barred with grayish brown and dusky.

Range—"Breeds in northwestern British Columbia, southwestern Yukon, and adjoining parts of Alaska south at least to southern Alberta. In winter down the Mississippi Valley to the Gulf States. Casual in California." (A. O. U.)

RED-SHOULDERED HAWKS
Buteo lineatus (GMELIN)

Other Names. Red-shoulder, Red-shouldered Buzzard, Hen Hawk, Big Chicken Hawk Winter Hawk, Singing Hawk.

There should be no difference of opinion, in view of the evidence presented by stomach examinations, regarding the economic status of the average Red-shouldered Hawk, of whatever geographical subspecies. *It is a decidedly beneficial species* from the agriculturalists' viewpoint, but it is, unfortunately, seldom given the credit it deserves, because of the persistency of the prejudice against *all* Hawks caused by the misdemeanors of a few species or individuals of some species. Dr. A. K. Fisher, forty years ago, summed up the situation with regard to the Red-shoulder when he stated that 65% of its food consists of destructive rodents while less than 2% consists of poultry, and all later studies bear out the accuracy of his deductions. Many cases have been known where this species has nested for years within sight of large poultry farms without its having taken a single chicken, while examinations of the nests in such locations have shown the food of the young to be very largely made up of meadow mice or ground squirrels, both of which rodents cause tremendous damage annually to agricultural interests. *The Red-shouldered Hawk should be protected at all times* except in the case of the occasional individual which develops a taste for poultry; such birds, however, are usually comparatively easy to control.

Recent reports indicate that the Red-bellied Hawk (the western race of the Red-shouldered) is greatly reduced in numbers, and is in need of rigid protection to prevent its early extinction.

Adult Red-shouldered Hawks are fairly easy of identification in the field. They have the typical buteonine outlines and the sluggish habits of the group; they are intermediate in size between the larger Red-tail and the smaller Broad-winged Hawk. The rufous shoulder patch, while brighter in adults, is also present to some extent in immature birds and is a most noticeable and distinctive field mark; it may usually be detected when the bird is perched as well as when, in circling, the upper surface of the wings is visible. The breast of the adult is quite evenly colored with rufous (yellowish buff in the Florida races, darker and richer in the Red-bellied Hawk), lightening but little on the throat and belly. The black tail crossed by several narrow white lines distinguishes the adult from all its relatives. The white bars on the primaries are wider towards the bases of the feathers and when seen from below seem to blend together to form a "luminous spot" which is considered a good field mark by some observers; the rest of the under surface of the wings is more heavily barred but the "wrist-mark" is seldom conspicuous.

The Red-shoulder is more a bird of the forested areas than the slightly larger and heavier appearing Red-tail. It is less often seen perched in conspicuous places nor does it soar as continuously as the latter bird. Immatures are much like young Red-tails or Broad-wings but the streaking of the under parts is more evenly distributed in the Red-shoulder and the dusky rufous upper wing coverts show in flight and usually when the bird is perched. The young Red-tail usually shows an unmarked area on the breast and a wide but broken abdominal band of blackish streaks; the tail of the Broad-wing has fewer but much wider whitish bars; in Swainson's Hawk the white of the belly extends up toward the back, suggesting a white rump when seen from the side while the bird is in flight.

The Red-shoulder's call is an easily recognized whistle, loud, clear, high-pitched and screaming, *kee-you, kee-you,* repeated several times and like one of the Blue Jay; it is never wheezy or windy like that of the Red-tail.

FEEDING HABITS

The Red-shouldered Hawk feeds very largely upon injurious rodents. A. T. Wayne (1910) says that Florida Red-shoulders are very fond of water snakes, but they also catch chickens and even grown fowls, though their principal food is composed of mice, frogs, and snakes, in South Carolina and neighboring states. F. S. Hersey (1923) found a 15-inch garter snake, the head and part of another of similar size, both hind legs of two frogs, a small turtle, three legs and a bill of Ruffed Grouse chicks, and a quantity of mouse hair, in the crop and stomach of a single Northern Red-shoulder, which gives some idea of the voracity of these birds as well as of the catholicity of their tastes. J. B. Dixon (1928) found young rabbits, several wood rats, and a mole, but no bird remains, about a nest of the Red-bellied Hawk in California. G. M. Sutton (1929-a) states that in thirty stomachs of the Northern Red-shoulder from Pennsylvania he found no remains of either poultry or other birds. D. J. Nicholson (1930) states that the Florida Red-shoulder feeds mainly upon frogs and mammals; it also eats snakes and occasionally birds; crickets and grasshoppers are also taken. L. L. Snyder (1932) examined a series of stomachs from Ontario: mammals formed 19% of the food; birds, 9%; reptiles and batrachians, 49.5%; crawfish, 10%; insects, 12.5%. Allan Brooks (*in litt.*, 1931) states of the Red-bellied Hawk, "their prey is largely reptiles and they seem to be able to find snakes and frogs even in the middle of a California winter."

RESULTS OF EXAMINATIONS OF STOMACHS AND CROPS

Authority	Number Examined	Mammals	Poultry or Game	Other Birds	Other Vertebrates	Insects	Miscellaneous	Empty
Warren, B. H., 1890	57	44	0	2	5	2	0	4
Fisher, A. K., 1893	220	142	3	12	62	0	26	14
Bailey, B. H., 1918	4	2	0	1	1	3	0	0
Bryant, H. C., 1918, 1921 . .	3	1	0	0	0	2	0	0
Howell, A. H., 1924, 1927 .	38	4	1	4	31	13	5	0
Miller, W. DeW., *mss.*, 1929	32	16	1	2	12	16	0	0
Luttringer, L. A., Jr., 1930 .	?	22	1	0	0	0	0	0
Stoddard, H. L., 1931 . . .	7	2	0	0	5	5	0	0
Guthrie, J. E., 1931	2	1	0	0	0	2	0	0
Brooks, Allan, *in litt.*, 1931 . .	10	2	0	0	4	0	0	4
Pearson, T. G., 1933-b . . .	71	51	1	4	7	11	7	16
Totals	444	287	7	25	127	54	38	38

The A. O. U. Check-List recognizes five subspecies of *Buteo lineatus* in North America.

NORTHERN RED-SHOULDERED HAWK
Buteo lineatus lineatus (GMELIN)

Other Names. Red-shoulder, Red-shouldered Buzzard, Hen Hawk, Big Chicken Hawk, Winter Hawk, Singing Hawk.

Description—A typical Buteo, slightly smaller than the Red-tail. Length of male 17 to 23 inches, spread 32.5 to 44 inches; length of female 19 to 24 inches, spread 39 to 50 inches. Adult: Dark reddish brown above, flecked with whitish but appearing almost black at a distance; lesser upper wing coverts or "shoulders" rufous or chestnut brown; under parts white finely cross-barred with rufous, darkest across breast; flight feathers blackish crossed with narrow white bars, this barring showing indistinctly when viewed from below; tail black with four to six very narrow white bars, only four of which may be visible in the field. Immature: Less rufous than adult; tail indistinctly barred with dark gray and brownish; under parts whitish or buffy evenly streaked, not barred, with dark brown.

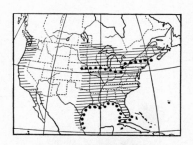

**RED-SHOULDERED
HAWKS**
Ruled Area—Breeding Range
Dotted Lines—Boundaries of
Winter Range

Range—"Breeds from Ontario, southern Quebec, Nova Scotia, and Prince Edward Island south to southern Kansas, northeastern Tennessee, and North Carolina and west to the edge of the Great Plains. Winters from central Iowa, Illinois, Indiana, southern Ohio, southern Ontario, central New York, southern New Hampshire, and southern Vermont, south to the Gulf coast and Texas." (A. O. U.)

FLORIDA RED-SHOULDERED HAWK
Buteo lineatus alleni RIDGWAY
Other Name. Southern Red-shoulder.

Description—Slightly smaller than *B. l. lineatus;* adults lighter colored and immatures darker. Adults may be distinguished by their grayish white heads with no rufous feather edges, by the grayer tone of the shoulder patch and the much lighter faintly barred yellowish buff under parts. Immatures can be distinguished only by their smaller size and darker coloration.

Range—"Lower Austral Zone of the Southern States from Oklahoma, Arkansas, Alabama, and South Carolina to Louisiana and southeastern Florida.

INSULAR RED-SHOULDERED HAWK
Buteo lineatus extimus BANGS
Other Name. Everglade Red-shoulder.

Description—Very similar to *B. l. alleni* but perhaps averages a little paler and slightly smaller.

Range—"Florida Keys." (A. O. U.) Mr. A. C. Bent writes me: "It breeds very sparingly, if at all, on the Keys, but it is an abundant breeder all over the southern third of mainland Florida."

TEXAS RED-SHOULDERED HAWK
Buteo lineatus texanus BISHOP

Description—Similar to *B. l. elegans* but averaging much larger; head and neck more rufous and breast usually spotted with buffy and with much more conspicuous shaft lines on breast feathers; much more richly colored below than *B. l. lineatus.* Immatures have the lower parts more buffy and the dark markings more numerous than young Northern Red-shoulders and they are more buffy but with less heavy markings than young Florida Red-shoulders.

Range—"Central southern Texas south into Tamaulipas, Mexico." (A. O. U.)

RED-BELLIED HAWK
Buteo lineatus elegans CASSIN
Other Names. Red-breasted Hawk, Squalling Hawk.

Description—Considerable individual variation; in extreme cases the whole under plumage is a rich dark reddish, almost obliterating the usually contrasting markings; the barring of the wings is conspicuous, however, and the tail is much as in the typical Northern Red-shoulder.

Range—"Resident in the Austral zones of California, chiefly in the San Joaquin and Sacramento valleys and lowlands of the San Diegan district from Marin and Shasta counties south to northwestern Lower California." (A. O. U.) "Southern British Columbia south to northern Lower California and northwestern Mexico." (Peters.)

BROAD-WINGED HAWK
Buteo platypterus platypterus (VEILLOT)

Other Names. Broad-winged Buzzard, Broad-wing, Chicken Hawk, Little Hawk.

The Broad-winged Hawk feeds largely upon insects, especially upon large destructive caterpillars and upon grasshoppers, both of which are injurious to agriculture or forestry, and upon mice whose destructive qualities are well known; it also eats many frogs and toads, which are beneficial or negative in their relations to Man; it very rarely molests birds of any kind. *It is therefore a decidedly beneficial species and one which should be given complete protection at all times.*

The Broad-winged Hawk appears to be quite gregarious in migration, flights of dozens or even hundreds being sometimes observed. At certain favored spots in the Appalachian Mountains, under favorable weather conditions, large numbers of this species are shot while migrating, a practice which is especially deplorable in view of the very beneficial feeding habits of this Hawk.

The Broad-wing is one of the tamest and most unsuspicious of Hawks, often allowing quite close approach. It spends much of its time sitting quietly among the branches of a tree within the forest, sometimes with hunched shoulders and drooping head, and it is doubtless often passed by unobserved when its more active relatives would be noted. It is a typical small Buteo, showing all the characteristics of the group except that it soars less at a considerable elevation or for a prolonged period. It has the chunky body, short square-ended or "fan-shaped" tail, fairly long but broad and round-ended wings, and sluggish movements of its tribe. When hunting, it sometimes hovers like a Sparrow Hawk or a diminutive Rough-leg. Its ordinary call, given both when in flight and when at rest, is a drawling, slurred, high-pitched whistle, *chuck-ke-e-e-e* or *pss-whee-e*, much like the note of a Wood Pewee; it has been likened to a steam whistle that "peters out" at the end.

The Broad-wing is decidedly smaller than the Red-tail, Red-shoulder and Swainson's Hawks, the other Buteos with which it is most commonly associated.

BROAD-WINGED HAWK

Adults at left and in flight, immature at right

It most nearly agrees in size with the Cooper's Hawk but its outline is very different from this typical Accipiter with its short wings and long tail. The Broad-wing's flight feathers are creamy white below with dark tips and the broad white tail bars are diagnostic. The Broad-wing usually shows a light eyebrow and a dark moustache. Young Broad-wings are very much like young Red-shoulders and Red-tails in general appearance but can usually be distinguished by their size, notes, and actions. Adults may be differentiated by size; they are also grayer above, and lack all rufous markings on either shoulders or tail; the under parts are rather evenly marked, lacking the zoning of the Red-tail, and are a duller shade of brown than those of the Red-shoulder.

FEEDING HABITS

The Broad-winged Hawk seldom eats birds and almost never touches poultry. J. J. Audubon (1840–44) says that he found wood frogs, portions of small snakes, together with feathers and the hair of several species of quadrupeds, in stomachs which he examined. A. K. Fisher (1893) states that a considerable part of their food in August and September consists of the larvae of certain large moths. F. L. Burns (1911) lists among their food hares and rabbits, red squirrels, chipmunks, various mice and shrews, weasels; birds from the size of a Flicker down; lizards, small snakes, frogs and toads; larvae of moths, beetles, locusts, grasshoppers, dragonflies, millipeds, spiders, ants; crabs, crawfish, and earthworms. William Brewster (1925) says they seem to prefer toads to any other food, in the Umbagog region of New England. E. H. Forbush (1927) adds crabs to the list of their foods. L. A. Luttringer, Jr., (1930) found only mice, grasshoppers and crickets in a small series from Pennsylvania. P. L. Errington (in litt., 1930) found remains of six mammals, a bird, a snake, and a large number of insects, in material collected at nests in Wisconsin. Townsend Godsey (1931) reports that Ernest Schwarz examined eight stomachs from Missouri and found only snakes and rodents.

RESULTS OF EXAMINATIONS OF STOMACHS AND CROPS

Authority	Number Examined	Mammals	Poultry or Game	Other Birds	Other Vertebrates	Insects	Miscellaneous	Empty
Warren, B. H., 1890	12	4	0	3	4	1	1	0
Fisher, A. K., 1893	65	28	0	2	24	30	6	7
Dunn, J. O., 1895	2	0	0	0	1	2	1	0
Ramsden, C. T., 1911	1	0	0	0	1	0	0	0
Burns, F. L., 1911	115	48	0	11	39	45	15	7
Bailey, B. H., 1918	19	6	0	0	4	18	0	0
Crabb, E. D., 1921	1	0	0	0	0	1	0	0
Hallinan, Thomas, 1924	1	0	0	0	1	0	0	0
Miller, W. DeW., mss., 1929	13	2	0	0	5	6	0	2
Snyder, L. L., 1932	23	6	0	1	5	9	1	4
Howell, A. H., 1932	2	1	0	0	1	2	1	0
Totals	254	95	0	17	85	114	25	20

SWAINSON'S HAWK
Adult male in light phase on stump, immature on rock, dark and light phases in flight

Description—One of the smallest of the buteonine Hawks, about the size of the rare and very local Short-tailed Hawk of Florida and the equally local Mexican Goshawk of the Texas borderland. Length of male 13.5 to 16.5 inches, spread 32 to 38 inches; length of female 15 to 19 inches, spread 33.5 to 39 inches. Adult: Above dark grayish brown; below whitish heavily barred with brown; throat white; wings silvery or creamy white below with black tips to flight feathers; tail with two or three rather conspicuous broad white bands. Immature: Under parts buffy streaked with brownish and with a white throat; several rather indistinct blackish bars on the grayish brown tail. The Broad-wing usually shows a fairly well marked brown moustache and a light colored, almost white, superciliary line or "eyebrow."

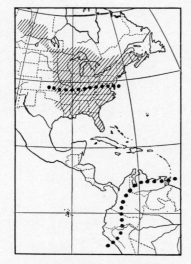

BROAD-WINGED HAWK
Ruled Area—Breeding Range
Dotted Lines—Boundaries of
Winter Range

Range—"Breeds from central Alberta, central Saskatchewan, southern Manitoba, Ontario, central Quebec, New Brunswick, and Cape Breton Island south to the Gulf coast and central Texas, mainly east of the Mississippi. Winters from southern Florida and southern Mexico through Central America to Colombia, Venezuela, and Peru; rarely farther north (reported from Connecticut, New Jersey, West Virginia, Ohio, Indiana, and Illinois). Recorded also from Cuba, Haiti, and Porto Rico." (A. O. U.) "Winters from southern Illinois and New Jersey to northern Venezuela, Colombia, Ecuador and Amazonian Peru." (Peters.) Representative races are also found in the West Indies.

SWAINSON'S HAWK
Buteo swainsoni BONAPARTE

Other Names. Prairie Hawk, Prairie Buzzard, Grasshopper Hawk, Gopher Hawk, Hen Hawk, Brown Hawk, Black Hawk.

The Swainson's Hawk destroys great quantities of field mice, gophers and ground squirrels as well as grasshoppers and other lowly but decidedly injurious creatures, so that *it is one of our most beneficial Hawks and it should be given complete protection at all times.* That it often lives in complete harmony with smaller birds is shown by the frequency with which other species build their nests in the same trees with Swainson's Hawks. On the very rare occasions when an individual may acquire a taste for poultry, it should be easy to control, for it is generally a sluggish and unsuspicious bird. Its tameness, indeed, has led to its serious diminution in numbers in many regions, for unfortunately not being protected by law or public opinion, it is heedlessly and needlessly slaughtered.

The Swainson's Hawk prefers open prairies, coursing over them with slow, rather sluggish, circling flight until it sights its prey, when it suddenly is transformed into an alert and skilful hunter. Frequently it sits perched on a fence post or other low observation point for long periods of time, watching for rodents or insects, and at such times it may often be approached quite closely. At times it may be seen hopping about on the ground in a sprightly manner while in pursuit of grass-hoppers or other insects. At other times it catches flying insects while on the wing, for I once watched a number of these birds busily "hawking" for adult dobson flies in the canyon of Yellowstone River; the insects were caught in the talons of the Hawk and eaten while the bird continued its flight.

In typical adult plumage the Swainson's Hawk is most likely to be mistaken for a Red-tailed Hawk, but it is grayer above and has a slaty gray tail crossed with numerous darker bars, instead of a red tail. The considerable unmarked buffy area on the under surface of the wings is one of the best field marks. The white throat and nearly white or buffy belly, separated by a wide pectoral band of chestnut or grayish brown, is unlike the evenly marked reddish under parts of the adult Red-shoulder but considerably like some plumages of the Red-tail. The Swain-son, however, almost always shows a light gray tail, lightest at the base, even when the numerous narrow bands cannot be distinguished. The white of the belly extends up on the flanks towards the back, showing in flight as a white spot either side of the rump, but it never shows white upper tail coverts as in the Marsh Hawk nor a white base to the tail as in the American Rough-leg. The young Red-shoulder resembles the young Swainson but its reddish shoulders are diagnostic. Young birds are harder to identify than adults, but the Swainson in any plumage has slightly narrower and more pointed wings than the Red-tail, Red-shoulder or the Rough-legs, and it gives the impression of a more slender or less robust bird. In melanistic examples this slight difference in form is of assistance in distinguish-ing this species. The Swainson's method of hunting, coursing low over the prairies, in search of insects and rodents, is more suggestive of the Rough-legs and the Marsh Hawk than of the high-soaring Red-tail or Red-shoulder.

Captain Bendire states that its call note "aside from a peculiar gurgling sound made while diving through the air, resembles the word *pi-tick*, *pi-tick* frequently repeated."

FEEDING HABITS

Elliott Coues (1874) says of Swainson's Hawk, "their prey is ordinarily nothing larger than gophers.—I scarcely think they are smart enough to catch birds very often.—Those I shot after midsummer all had their craws stuffed with grass-hoppers." H. W. Henshaw (1875) also reports "the crops of all those shot were crammed with grasshoppers." C. H. Merriam (1888) examined three stomachs which held respectively 106, 96 and 88 grasshoppers, and one of these also held the head of a meadow mouse. A. K. Fisher (1893) says that besides many insects, it eats small rodents, reptiles, batrachians, and occasionally birds, but rarely touches poultry. Mrs. F. M. Bailey (1902) says it feeds almost entirely upon small rodents, principally striped gophers and mice, together with grasshoppers and crickets. E. S. Cameron (1913) says it prefers frogs, grasshoppers, and mice, in the order named, to any other food, in Montana. Norman Criddle (1915) states that its food is 80% noxious rodents but that it also eats young Grouse, Meadowlarks and other birds, and occasionally young poultry in British Columbia. J. A. Munro (1929) says that in Alberta it feeds largely upon ground squirrels. P. G. Redington (1929) reports that the Bureau of Biological Survey examined forty-five stomachs from Washington State which showed that 90% of the food remains was ground squirrels; 10% was snakes and grasshoppers or other insects. A. C. Bent (*mss.*, 1933) states, "I can find no evidence that this Hawk ever attacks poultry or game birds, and most observers agree that it seldom if ever kills birds of any kind."

RESULTS OF EXAMINATIONS OF STOMACHS AND CROPS

Authority	Number Examined	Mammals	Poultry or Game	Other Birds	Other Vertebrates	Insects	Miscellaneous	Empty
Merriam, C. H., 1888	3	1	0	0	0	3	0	0
Fisher, A. K., 1893	18	7	0	0	6	8	0	3
Bailey, B. H., 1918	2	0	0	0	0	2	0	0
Munro, J. A., 1929	10	0	0	1	0	10	0	0
Brooks, Allan, *in litt.*, 1931 .	11	2	1	0	0	8	0	0
Totals	44	10	1	1	6	31	0	3

Description—This species, of typical Buteo proportions, shows wide variation in coloring. Length of male 19 to 21 inches, spread 47 to 51 inches; length of female 19 to 22 inches, spread 47 to 57 inches. Adult male in light or "typical" plumage: Upper parts nearly uniform dark grayish brown, somewhat lighter on rump; tail tinged with hoary and with about nine to twelve narrow indistinct dusky bands, which show more clearly on under surface; forehead, chin and throat, white; breast bright chestnut with black streaks, forming a wide and continuous pectoral band; balance of under parts silvery whitish or cream colored, more or less spotted and barred with brown; a broad unmarked buffy area on under coverts of wings; "wrist mark" often inconspicuous or wanting. Adult female in light phase: Very similar to male but pectoral band grayish brown instead of chestnut. Immature: Entire upper parts dark brown, the feather with tawny edges; head, neck and under parts buff or buffy white, streaked and blotched with blackish drop-shaped markings, especially across the breast; wings and tail indistinctly barred with darker brown. Dark phase: Extreme melanistic examples have nearly the entire plumage sooty brown, though the tail usually shows numerous ashy bars; there are

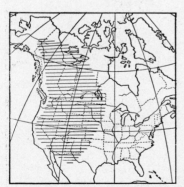

SWAINSON'S HAWK
Ruled Area—Breeding Range

ZONE-TAILED HAWK
Adults

various intermediate shades and patterns between the light phase and the extreme dark phase.

Range—"Breeds from interior British Columbia, Fort Yukon, Great Slave Lake, and Manitoba south to northern Mexico. Winters in southern South America, only occasionally north of the Equator. Casual in Quebec, Ontario, Michigan, Vermont, New York, Maine, Massachusetts, and Florida." (A. O. U.)

ZONE-TAILED HAWK

Buteo albonotatus KAUP

Other Names. Zone-tail, Band-tail, Band-tailed Hawk, Band-tailed Buzzard.

The rather tame and sluggish Zone-tailed Hawk is an interesting and harmless species found in the United States only in a restricted area close to the Mexican boundary. The few stomach examinations available show that it does occasionally eat birds, but field observations would indicate that this is not a common practice and that it is usually too slow moving and clumsy to capture such active creatures as most birds. Because of its rarity and local distribution *it should be given complete protection.*

The Zone-tailed Hawk shares many of the traits of the commoner Buteos, soaring high in air above its hunting grounds, easily supported on its very ample wings and wide tail, wheeling and plunging and giving its loud and piercing cry at intervals. In search of prey these birds often frequent canyons "where they circle about scouring the cliffs, or, mounting high in the air, dive screaming almost to the water at the bottom," and at other times their actions are much like those of a Marsh Hawk while hunting. Occasionally, when in pursuit of fish, they hover over the water like an Osprey or a huge Kingfisher. Their cry is said to be very much like that of the Broad-winged Hawk but more piercing and not so highly pitched.

The Zone-tail should be easily recognized in its chosen habitat, by its generally black plumage and the three whitish or ashy bands of varying width on its tail. The Mexican Black Hawk shows a single wide and very noticeable white bar across the middle of its tail and whitish spots at the base of the primaries as seen from below. There is considerable resemblance in style, coloration, and manner of flight, to the Turkey Vulture, which has, however, a much smaller, less noticeable and naked head, and an all black tail.

FEEDING HABITS

E. A. Mearns (1886) says the Zone-tailed Hawk in Arizona captures lizards, frogs, fishes, and "other desirable articles of raptorial diet." Mrs. F. M. Bailey (1902) says this species eats small mammals, lizards, frogs and fishes, including

SENNETT'S WHITE-TAILED HAWK
Adults perched and above, immature in centre

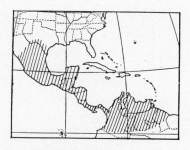

SENNETT'S WHITE-
TAILED HAWK
Ruled Area—Breeding Range

tinct dusky bars and with a rusty tip. Young birds are sometimes quite dark but true melanism is practically unknown in this species.

Range—"Lower Austral Zone of middle Texas south to Colombia." (A. O. U.)

"Southwestern United States (Lower Rio Grande Valley) south through Mexico and Central America to northwestern South America (Colombian Andes and Andes of Merida, Venezuela)." (Peters, 1931.)

Two other representative races are found in South America.

SHORT-TAILED HAWK

Buteo brachyurus VIEILLOT

Other Names. Short-tailed Buzzard, Little Black Hawk.

The Short-tailed Hawk is one of the rarest Hawks in North America and is found in the United States only in a limited region on the Florida peninsula, where it has apparently never been common and where today it is perhaps seriously threatened with early extirpation unless active measures are taken for its preservation. It is probably harmless in its feeding habits, but is far too rare to be considered from an economic standard. It is one of the few birds which exhibit true dichromatism, that is, it has two distinctly different color phases which are irrespective of age or sex, and it is of especial interest to scientists for that reason. *Every effort should be made to save this interesting little bird from extinction in the United States.*

The Short-tailed Hawk is unsuspicious and gentle in disposition and attractive in appearance. It is an expert on the wing and often sails for a long time, in typical Buteo fashion, high above the swamps and woodlands, apparently without a movement of its extended wings and tail. It should be easily recognized from its shape and size and its characteristic color patterns. Its alarm note consists of "a few cackling notes, somewhat like the Red-shouldered Hawk." H. W. Brandt (1924) gives an interesting account of the nesting of this rare and little known species in Florida.

The Broad-winged Hawk is the only other buteonine Hawk approaching this species in size, which is found in Florida, but its coloration is very different, its barred or streaked under parts and the characteristic banding of the tail of the adult easily distinguishing it in the field.

FEEDING HABITS

Very little is known about the food of the Short-tailed Hawk. In most cases

SHORT-TAILED HAWK

Light and dark phases

where specimens have been collected no study has been made of the stomach contents, and most collectors have apparently been too anxious to kill the birds for specimens to pay much attention to their habits. A. K. Fisher (1893) says, "it is not improbable that it resembles the Broad-winged Hawk in habits as well as in the character of its food." A stomach examined by Dr. Fisher in 1896 contained the feet and other remains of a Sharp-shinned Hawk, according to manuscript records in the Bureau of Biological Survey, but it hardly seems probable that a bird of the type of the Short-tailed Hawk could have captured and killed such a swift-flying Raptor as a Sharp-shin if the latter was in good physical condition, and it is possible that this food record represents carrion rather than a freshly killed bird. Thomas Hallinan (1924) shot a specimen in the Panama Canal Zone which was eating two 14-inch ground lizards and which had the remains of a small bird in its stomach. A. C. Bent (*mss.*, 1933) says, "probably snakes, frogs, lizards, small mammals and small birds are eaten." To this list of "probabilities" we would add, by analogy with other Buteos, insects of various kinds.

Description—A small but typical Buteo, of two very different color phases, so unlike as to have been considered as different species by early ornithologists. Apparently no intermediate stages exist and this is true dichromatism and not melanism which is so common in many species of this genus like the Swainson's Hawk, the Western Red-tail, and the two Rough-legs. Length about 17 inches, spread about 35 inches. Adult in light phase: Above dark slaty gray or grayish brown; under parts pure white except sides of breast which are rufous brown, forming a partial collar open in front; tail barred with about seven bands of black and white above and grayish below; under surface of wings shows primaries largely white with black tips, and barred secondaries. Adult in dark phase (known as the Little Black Hawk): Dark brownish black all over except whitish forehead, occasional concealed spots or bars on under parts, grayish under surface of primaries, and grayish tail barred with black.

SHORT-TAILED HAWK
Ruled Area—Breeding Range

Range—"Florida, eastern Mexico, and Central America south to Peru, Bolivia, and Brazil." (A. O. U.)

AMERICAN ROUGH-LEGGED HAWK
Buteo lagopus sancti-johannis (GMELIN)

Other Names. American Rough-leg, Rough-legged Buzzard, Ruf-leg, Black Hawk, Mouse Hawk, Squalling Hawk.

The American Rough-legged Hawk is northern in distribution, being found in the United States only in winter. As long ago as 1840, Audubon wrote of this bird, "the number of meadow mice which this species destroys ought, one might

AMERICAN ROUGH-LEGGED HAWK

Light and dark phases

think, to ensure it the protection of every husbandman; but so far is this from being the case, that in America it is shot on all occasions, simply because its presence frightens Mallards and other Ducks, which would alight in the ponds, on the shores of which the wily gunner is concealed; and in England it is caught in traps as well as shot, perhaps for no better reason than because it is a hawk." The data given below on its feeding habits should prove that this species has a very high rank as a beneficial one, and *it should receive rigid protection at all times as an extremely valuable check upon our injurious rodents.* The bird is easily recognizable and there is no excuse for killing it "by mistake" for another species.

The American Rough-leg is a large Hawk of typical Buteo outline, notably sluggish in its movements. Its favorite hunting grounds are wherever meadow mice abound. It is most commonly observed perched on a large rock or low tree or post overlooking grassy meadows or coursing back and forth low over the fields and marshes. It is often seen thus engaged, at dusk, and it is the most crepuscular of our Hawks. Its flight is usually slow, measured and noiseless, and, with its habit of hunting at dusk, suggests that of some great Owl. When soaring, the wings are spread to their greatest extent and the outer primaries are curved upward slightly and are separated like the fingers of an open hand. It has the accipitrine habit of taking a few wing strokes, sailing a short distance, and repeating, but its heavy deliberation is very different from the dashing flight of the Accipiters. During direct flight the tail is usually closed, but, when soaring, it is spread open like a fan. Occasionally the bird hovers in one spot, sometimes dropping its legs as though about to pounce upon its prey, and then, apparently changing its mind, drawing them up again under its tail. When wind conditions are just right it sometimes will hold itself stationary in one spot in the air, without hovering, for some moments, in an up-current above a hillside. When perched, it sits very erect but low, and its closed wings extend nearly to the end of its tail. While usually a silent bird in its winter habitat in the United States, on its breeding grounds it is so noisy that it is known as the Squalling Hawk on the coast of Labrador. One of its calls has been described as a loud squealing like the neighing of a colt but more shrill and savage in tone, another as a high-pitched *ke-ah, ke-ah, ke-yak.* The nest is usually built in a low tree or among loose rocks on an exposed ledge.

The American Rough-leg in typical light plumage should be unmistakable but melanistic individuals call for discrimination, especially in the West where melanism is common in the Western Red-tail, Swainson's Hawk, and the Ferruginous Rough-leg. The Rough-legs are characterized by their large size, relatively broad wings rather pointed at the tips (for Buteos), and rather long tails (for Buteos). In the typical light phase the American Rough-leg is noticeable for its conspicuous masses of contrasting dark and light areas, being characterized by the broad, blackish abdominal band, wide band on the tail, the conspicuous "wrist-mark," and dark tips to all the flight feathers. The dark phase may be all dark but the bird usually shows a white base to the tail, thus resembling somewhat the so-called "Ring-tailed Eagle," the young of the Golden Eagle. The black phase of the Ferruginous Rough-leg is very much like its northern relative but it usually shows more or less rufous mixed with its black. Both Rough-legs show a whitish area at the base of the primaries but this is more noticeable in the Ferruginous Rough-leg. In the light phase the latter species shows white under parts with chestnut thighs, a grayish or brownish tail, and rufous shoulders. The dark phase of the Western Red-tail usually shows considerable rufous in the tail of the adult and the bird averages slightly smaller than the Rough-leg; the immature Red-tail has a banded tail. Swainson's Hawk is still smaller and the tail is usually grayer with numerous narrow bands.

FEEDING HABITS

All authorities seem to agree that meadow mice and similar destructive rodents form the bulk of the food of the American Rough-legged Hawk and that it very rarely molests birds of any kind, large or small. Thomas Nuttall (1832) gives their food as mice, moles and frogs but speaks of their "sometimes contenting themselves with crabs and shellfish when nothing better offered." J. J. Audubon (1840–1844) says, "it feeds principally on moles, mice, and other small quadrupeds." H. W. Henshaw (1875) found only mice in eleven stomachs from Utah but

RESULTS OF EXAMINATIONS OF STOMACHS AND CROPS

Authority	Number Examined	Mammals	Poultry or Game	Other Birds	Other Vertebrates	Insects	Miscellaneous	Empty
Henshaw, H. W., 1875	11	11	0	0	0	0	0	0
Aughey, Samuel, 1878	1	1	0	0	1	1	0	0
Warren, B. H., 1890	11	11	0	0	0	0	0	0
Fisher, A. K., 1893	49	45	0	0	1	1	0	4
Nash, C. W., 1898	32	30	0	0	1	1	0	0
Bailey, B. H., 1918	13	7	0	0	1	1	0	5
Dice, L. R., 1920	1	1	0	0	0	0	0	0
Huey, L. M., 1924	1	1	0	0	0	1	0	0
Miller, W. DeW., mss., 1929	3	2	0	0	0	1	0	0
Munro, J. A., 1929	2	2	0	0	0	0	0	0
Luttringer, L. A., Jr., 1930	7	2	1	0	0	0	0	5
Errington, P. L., in litt., 1930	3	3	0	0	0	3	0	0
Brooks, Allan, in litt., 1931	8	7	0	0	0	0	0	1
Snyder, L. L., 1932	58	44	0	0	2	3	3	6
Austin, O. L., Jr., 1932	2	2	0	0	0	0	0	0
Bur. Biol. Surv., 1893-1931	?	52	0	9	2	7	0	?
Totals	202+	221	1	9	8	19	3	21+

says that this species is reported to eat Ducks crippled by gunners. A. K. Fisher (1893) says, "it is credited with feeding on snakes, lizards, frogs and toads, though the writer has never found the remains of any of these animals in the stomachs examined." E. S. Cameron (1907) says that prairie dogs are a favorite food in Montana, while A. A. Saunders (1911) thinks gophers are its principal food there.

L. R. Dice (1920) examined a bird from interior Alaska which held four young shrews, and states that although Ducks and Ptarmigan were abundant, they showed no fear of the Hawks. F. C. Lincoln (1920) described one as feeding upon a house cat which had been killed a week previously by Mr. Lincoln. Bernard Hantzsch (1929) says that in northeastern Labrador their food consists chiefly of banded lemmings and white-footed mice. C. W. Townsend collected thirty-two pellets at a roosting place in Massachusetts, which contained remains of thirty-nine mice, three shrews, three birds, and some insects.

Description—A large Hawk of two intergrading color phases showing great individual variation. Length of male 19 to 22 inches, spread 48 to 52 inches; length of female 21 to 24 inches, spread 52 to 56 inches. Legs (tarsi) feathered to the toes. Adult in light phase: Head, neck and back light buffy or creamy white, lightly or heavily streaked with brown; base of tail and under surface of wings mostly white but with broad black tips to tail and flight feathers; a prominent "wrist-mark" and usually a broad and more or less solid dark brown or blackish abdominal band which is quite diagnostic when present. Some old birds show merely a pattern-less admixture of dark and light streaks with no distinctive features except the white basal two-thirds of the tail. Adult in dark phase: Practically black or dark sooty brown all over, though usually showing a white forehead, whitish or dusky areas on the inner webs of the flight feathers, and considerable white at the base of the tail, even in the darkest examples. There are all grades between these two extreme plumages. Immature: The abdominal band is more solid and more clearly defined than in typical light adults.

Range—"Breeds chiefly in the Hudsonian Zone from the Aleutian Islands, northwestern Alaska (Arctic coast), Victoria Island, southwestern Baffin Island, northern Quebec (Ungava), and northeastern Labrador to northern Alberta, north shore of the Gulf of St. Lawrence, and Newfoundland. Winters from southern British Columbia, Colorado, Minnesota, the northern boundary of the United States, and southern Ontario south to southern California, southern New Mexico, Texas, Louisiana, and North Carolina. Accidental on St. George Island, Pribilof Islands" (A.O.U.). Accidental in Bermuda (Bradlee).

"The Siberian race *pallidus* has been collected at St. Michaels, Alaska. A male shot there by E. W. Nelson on September 16, 1879, is so much closer to Asiatic birds (*pallidus*) than to the American subspecies that I consider it to be *pallidus;* a female without definite locality other than 'West Coast, Alaska,' taken by J. W. Johnson, April 10, 1886, is intermediate in color between *s.-johannis* and *pallidus*, but is large like the latter form; a male taken at St. Michaels by L. M. Turner, April 10, 1876, agrees in color with *s.-johannis* but in size with *pallidus*. The race *pallidus* is larger than *s.-johannis* and has the pale margins of the feathers of the upper parts lighter and broader than in the latter, especially in the young birds" (Friedmann, 1934).

Other representative races are found in northern Europe and Asia.

AMERICAN ROUGH-
LEGGED HAWK
Ruled Area—Breeding Range
Dotted Lines—Boundaries of
Winter Range

FERRUGINOUS ROUGH-LEG

Light and dark phases

FERRUGINOUS ROUGH-LEG
Buteo regalis (GRAY)

Other Names. Chap Hawk, Squirrel Hawk, California Squirrel Hawk, Gopher Hawk, Rusty Hawk, Rusty Squirrel Hawk, Prairie Eagle, Eagle Hawk.

The beautiful great Ferruginous Rough-leg is found in many suitable places throughout the western states, where it is an important enemy of destructive rodents, seldom eating birds of any kind and almost never touching poultry. In spite of its great potential value to agriculture, it is one of the birds which seems to be an especially attractive, in fact an almost irresistible, target for the thoughtless man with a gun, and many are killed annually, for no better reasons than that they are easy to kill and are not protected by law or public sentiment. *It should be given complete protection at all times* and a widespread campaign of education should be carried on to stop the needless slaughter and rapid decrease of this fine species.

The habits of the Ferruginous Rough-leg or Squirrel Hawk, as it might well be named, are much like those of its near relative the American Rough-leg, but it is more southern and western in distribution. It is essentially a bird of the open prairie regions and of the adjacent "bad lands," where it may often be seen as it watches for its prey from a fence post or other slight elevation, standing on one leg for considerable periods of time, the other leg drawn up among the body feathers. If facing the observer, the white throat and breast and whitish head are conspicuous, contrasting with the chestnut on shoulders, flanks and thighs. As it leaves its perch its flight is heavy and with slow wing-beats but after attaining some elevation it soars easily. At other times it hunts like a Marsh Hawk, "winnowing low over the ground with almost laborious movement" and picking up its prey as it passes along. At such times it shows two areas of light color on the upper surface of its brown wings, as well as a whitish tail, these forming distinctive field marks. When flying overhead the bird appears nearly white below but with a dark V-shaped mark formed by the chestnut and black thighs and legs, the apex of the V below the tail being formed by the closely approximated feet.

The Ferruginous Rough-leg, because of its size, is most likely to be confused with the American Rough-leg, the Red-tail, the Osprey, or one of the Eagles, but in the light phase it should be unmistakable. W. L. Dawson (1923) says, "the strong mingling of rusty brown above is distinctive in any adult plumage. The white of the under parts shading to rusty posteriorly is unique." In the dark phase it usually shows some chestnut spotting and the tail and wings are as in the typical bird. It is rather more slender appearing than the American Rough-leg and shows a proportionately longer tail. At close range its bill is much larger (broader at the base or "gape") than that of the American Rough-leg. It never shows the ochraceous tone nor the blackish abdominal band of the latter bird. The Osprey has white under parts but lacks all chestnut markings, the upper parts are nearly uniform brown, the tail is evenly barred, and the wings are longer and narrower proportionately. In the dark phase the Ferruginous Rough-leg may resemble the young or "ring-tailed" Golden Eagle but it is smaller, its wings are more pointed, and its tail longer in proportion to the bird's expanse.

FEEDING HABITS

The Ferruginous Rough-leg feeds very largely upon ground squirrels and other destructive rodents. Elliott Coues (1874) says that he found remains of pouched rats, wood mice, kangaroo mice and meadow mice in stomachs he examined and adds that in California this species feeds largely upon ground squirrels. A. K. Fisher (1893) expresses his opinion that they feed largely upon small mammals and reptiles. Mrs. F. M. Bailey (1902) says they eat crickets. E. S. Cameron (1914) says that they feed principally upon prairie dogs and mice, though they are not averse to snakes, in Montana; at one nest he found remains of nine prairie dogs, a rabbit, two bull snakes, and some remnants of Sharp-tailed Grouse and Western Meadowlarks; at another nest he found four prairie dog skulls, two bull snakes, a Sharp-tailed Grouse, a Magpie and a Meadowlark; he believed that they never took frogs. He once saw one catch a house cat and raise it twenty-five feet in the air before dropping its struggling booty. P. A. Taverner (1919) found "over a bushel of dried bones and scraps of gophers" near a nest in Alberta. Henry Grey (1925) found a ground squirrel and gophers in several stomachs which he examined. D. S. DeGroot (1927) states that this species is a conspicuous enemy of the California Clapper Rail, but his testimony is exceptional. A. C. Bent (mss., 1933) says its food "consists almost exclusively of mammals, ranging in size from jack rabbits to meadow mice; snakes, lizards and skinks are taken occasionally, as well as grasshoppers and crickets."

RESULTS OF EXAMINATIONS OF STOMACHS AND CROPS

Authority	Number Examined	Mammals	Poultry or Game	Other Birds	Other Vertebrates	Insects	Miscellaneous	Empty
Fisher, A. K., 1893	1	1	0	0	0	0	0	0
Bryant, H. C., 1913, 1918 . .	3	1	0	0	1	1	0	0
Pierce, W. M., 1919	1	0	0	0	1	0	0	0
Miller, W. DeW., mss., 1929.	1	1	0	0	0	0	0	0
Bur. Biol. Surv., 1893-1931. .	18	18	1	1	0	1	0	0
Totals	24	21	1	1	2	2	0	0

Description—A large Hawk with two intergrading color phases. Length 22.5 to 25 inches, spread about 56 inches. Adult in light phase: Above a mixture of blackish and chestnut, the latter predominating on shoulders and rump; tail noticeably pale, varying from reddish white above mottled with ashy, and yellowish white below, to almost a pure white, but usually whitest at the base darkening toward the end into an indistinct subterminal band; head streaked with black or brown but distinctly light in appearance at a little distance; below nearly pure white from bill to tail except for a few chestnut bars on belly and flanks, and a few black streaks on the breast; thighs ("flags") bright chestnut or rufous barred with black, as are the feathered tarsi which give the bird its name, and which form a marked contrast to the white breast and belly; wings with under surface largely white and with a whitish area on upper surface near the tip, which shows in flight; no cross-barring of the flight feathers. Immature: Above brownish gray with less rufous showing; legs and thighs much lighter; tail usually with about four dark bars. Melanistic individuals are common, some extreme cases being chocolate brown more or less variegated with rusty, but often with the light tail of the typical bird or the tail with several narrow white bands, and with a white area at the base of the primaries which shows in flight.

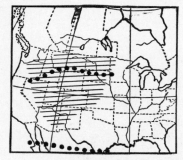

FERRUGINOUS
ROUGH-LEG
Ruled Area—Breeding Range
Dotted Lines—Boundaries of
Winter Range

Range—"Breeds from extreme southern Alberta and Manitoba to northeastern California, eastern Oregon, Utah, southern Arizona, New Mexico, and Kansas. Winters from California and Montana to Lower California and northern Mexico. Casual east to Wisconsin and Illinois." (A. O. U.) "The 'breeding record' [for California] is very unsatisfactory." (W. L. Dawson, 1923.)

HARRIS'S HAWK
Parabuteo unicinctus harrisi (AUDUBON)

Other Names. Black Hawk, Harris's Buzzard.

Harris's Hawk is a large dark-colored buteonine Hawk, of limited distribution in the United States where it is found only in a narrow area along the southern boundary from California to Mississippi, though it is comparatively common in some parts of this range. It is generally considered as a beneficial species or at the worst, as neutral in its economic relations, its sluggish habits seeming to preclude a diet of such active creatures as birds. It has undoubtedly diminished in numbers in recent years, through thoughtless killing, and it should be given the protection deserved by all Buteos.

Harris's Hawk should be easily recognized in the field. At a distance it may appear all dark except the tail which is white with a broad black band; at closer view it shows chestnut patches on shoulders, under wing coverts, and thighs. It is a bird of the chaparral, nesting in bushes or low trees, and it is decidedly terrestrial at times. It often perches quietly for considerable periods of time, or occupies itself with leisurely soaring about at a high altitude, in typical Buteo fashion. When soaring overhead, the white rump and base of the tail, with its broad black subterminal band and white tip, coupled with the sooty black body and the scattered chestnut areas on wing coverts and thighs, make identification easy. The Ferruginous Rough-leg in melanistic plumage shows some chestnut usually, but its tail

HARRIS'S HAWK

Adults

is largely brownish or grayish and lacks the contrasting black and white bands of Harris's Hawk. On the ground the latter bird shows some resemblance to the Black Vulture when seen at a distance, but as it rises in flight the white on the tail immediately identifies it. It is a rather noisy bird, a common note being "a low harsh *karr*, which becomes a long snarling cry when the bird is aroused."

FEEDING HABITS

But little definite information is available regarding the food of Harris's Hawk. G. B. Sennett (1879) found "mice, lizards, birds, and often the Mexican striped gopher" in crops of specimens from Texas. C. C. Nutting (1882) says that a specimen from Costa Rica was shot while carrying off a chicken. A. K. Fisher (1893) states that the food consists "largely of offal, the smaller reptiles and mammals, and occasionally birds." Mrs. F. M. Bailey (1902) reports finding eleven skulls of a wood rat, *Neotoma*, in a nest in Texas and later (1928) specifies cottontail rabbits, cotton rats, wood rats, ground squirrels, and field mice, as among the mammals taken. W. L. Dawson (1923) says that Harris's Hawk "has never been known to kill birds, let alone hens" in California. Loyes Miller (1925) reports finding the bodies of a Florida Gallinule and a Sora Rail on the edge of a nest of this species. G. F. Simmons (1925) gives its food as lizards, small snakes, cottontail rabbits, cotton rats, and field mice. Allan Brooks (*in litt.*, 1931) writes, "while in summer rabbits and cotton rats may make up the major portion of their diet, at other times wild fowl of various species are killed in large numbers and these may include birds larger than themselves, Night Herons being frequent victims."

RESULTS OF EXAMINATIONS OF STOMACHS AND CROPS

Authority	Number Examined	Mammals	Poultry or Game	Other Birds	Other Vertebrates	Insects	Miscellaneous	Empty
Fisher, A. K., 1893	6	5	0	0	0	1	0	1
Bur. Biol. Surv., *mss.* notes	1	1	0	0	0	0	0	0
Miller, Loyes, 1925	2	0	1	1	0	0	0	0
Brooks, Allan, *in litt.*, 1931	6	1	0	2	0	0	0	3
Totals	15	7	1	3	0	1	0	4

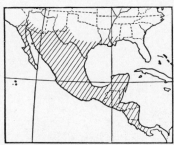

HARRIS'S HAWK
Ruled Area—Breeding Range

Description—Length of male 17.5 to 21 inches; length of female 21 to 24 inches, spread about 45 inches. Adult: General plumage sooty black or dark brown; shoulders, under wing coverts, and thighs, chestnut; rump tinged with chestnut; primaries black; tail coverts and basal half and a band at tip of tail, white; there is a small area of naked skin (the lores) between the bill and the eye and this, with the cere, is bright yellow. Immature: Head and neck streaked, body feathers with rusty edges; under parts ochraceous; more or less whitish and buffy streakings above

MEXICAN GOSHAWK

Adult at right, immature at left

and below; tailmore barred.

Range—"Lower Austral Zone in southeastern California, southern Arizona, southern New Mexico, southern Texas, Louisiana, and Mississippi south to Cape San Lucas and Panama. Accidental in Iowa." (A. O. U.)

A representative race occurs in South America, to Argentina.

MEXICAN GOSHAWK
Asturina plagiata plagiata Schlegel

Other Names. Mexican Star Buzzard, Gray Star Buzzard.

The interesting and handsome little Mexican Goshawk is a bird of restricted range in the United States, being seldom found far from the Mexican border. *It should be given complete protection*, as a rare species about whose habits all too little is known, and one which is probably harmless if not actually beneficial. It is unfortunate that it has been given the name "Goshawk," for its closest relationship lies with the rodent-eating buteonine Hawks and not with the bird-killing Accipiters, only its coloration suggesting a Goshawk. It has been aptly described as having the proportions of a Buteo, the coloration of a Goshawk, and the actions of a Falcon.

It is a bird of the open country, preferring the vicinity of water courses, and it is seldom found on the dry desert-like plains, hence its distribution is quite irregular even within the narrow range given below. It is swift and powerful in flight, with graceful and easily controlled motions which suggest a Falcon, though it is more given to soaring than are most Falcons. Captain Bendire says, "I have seen one of them dart to the ground with arrow-like swiftness to pick up some bird, lizard or rodent, continuing its flight without any stop whatever." It is a rather noisy bird at times. One of its notes is described as a loud *crurr, crurr* or *cree-u-u*, repeated several times and suggestive of the scream of a distant Peacock, but in the spring it frequently gives another note, of decidedly flute-like quality and resembling the spring note of the Long-billed Curlew.

FEEDING HABITS

The Mexican Goshawk is a species about whose feeding habits we know comparatively little. G. N. Lawrence (1874) quotes A. J. Grayson as saying its food consists of lizards, small snakes, field mice, etc., young Songbirds, young poultry and young game birds, and later (1875) quotes F. E. Sumichrast as writing that in Mexico "it lives on rats, birds, and insects." William Brewster (1883) says lizards, small squirrels, fish scales, the wing covers of beetles, and unrecognizable fur and bones of small rodents, were found in stomachs of specimens taken in Arizona by R. Stephens. C. E. Bendire (1892) says, "a good proportion of their food consists of beetles, large grasshoppers—and other insects—and I believe small birds form

MEXICAN BLACK HAWK

Adults

no inconsiderable portion of their food." Mrs. F. M. Bailey (1902) says that beetles and grasshoppers are caught while upon the wing. H. S. Swarth (1905) examined five stomachs of birds shot in Arizona: one held some young Doves, another remains of a Quail, and the rest held some large lizards. W. H. Hudson (1920) says that a closely related South American Hawk feeds largely if not exclusively upon fish. A. C. Bent (*mss.*, 1933) examined two Texas specimens, one of which held a small snake, the other a lizard.

Description—Length about 16 to 18 inches, spread 32 to 38 inches. Adult: Above plain ashy gray streaked or barred with darker, paler on head and darker toward rump; upper tail coverts (rump) white; tail blackish with two or three rather wide white bands and a white tip; under parts, except white chin and under tail coverts, very regularly and finely barred with gray and white, noticeably lighter in effect than the ashy gray back. Imma-

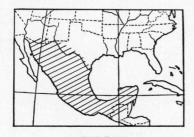

MEXICAN
GOSHAWK
Ruled Area—Breeding Range

ture: Upper parts sooty brown streaked with buffy on head and spotted on wings; rump white; tail grayish with six or seven black bands and a white tip; under parts broadly streaked with brown except on throat; sides and under wings buffy.

Range—"Southern Arizona, southern New Mexico, and Lower Rio Grande Valley south to Guatemala. Winters south of the United States. Accidental in southern Illinois." (A. O. U.)

Representative races are found south to Argentina.

MEXICAN BLACK HAWK

Urubitinga anthracina anthracina (LICHTENSTEIN)

Other Names. Anthracite Buzzard, Crab Hawk.

The rare and local Mexican Black Hawk is apparently a harmless if not an actively beneficial species, and *it should be given complete protection at all times*, as an interesting bird of striking appearance. Its food consists largely of crustaceans and the lower vertebrates, with birds only occasionally entering into its bill-of-fare.

The Mexican Black Hawk shows a preference for wooded country near water rather than for open prairie or desert regions and it is often found in forests, well concealed in the foliage. Its flight is described as swift and powerful. G. B. Thomas says that "in flight they excel any of the hawks, kites or falcons, except possibly the Swallow-tailed Kite." At times it soars like a typical Buteo, and at other times it sits quietly for long periods of time hidden among the branches of the trees. Often in flight the legs dangle like those of the White-tailed Kite. Its call, according to Captain Bendire, has a strong resemblance to the note of the Long-billed Curlew, and it has also been described as "a shrill *ker-r-r-re-e-e-e* like a policeman's whistle."

71

This species presents in the field an exceptionally broad wing with a small white mark at the base of the primaries which shows from below, and its white tail markings are also conspicuous and diagnostic. The Zone-tailed Hawk, another Black Hawk, has three light bands on its tail, diminishing in width toward the base, gray above and white below, which show plainly when the bird is seen from below, but less distinctly when viewed from above; the Mexican Black Hawk has a narrow white tip to the tail, a broad band in its middle, and a white base, separated by two broad black areas, which are conspicuous whether seen from above or below. "Apart from the resemblance in color," writes Allan Brooks, "the Mexican Black Hawk has no likeness to a Zone-tail; flight, shape of wing and hunting habits are almost entirely different. Sitting in the lower branches of some big cottonwood, almost invisible among the heavy foliage, the Black Hawk watches for its prey which consists largely of reptiles and batrachians. Only when its hunting is over will it mount into the air swinging aloft in effortless spirals and now the notable breadth of its wings is apparent. Probably no other American Hawk has so large a wing area in proportion to its size; from below the short diagonal white splash at the base of the primaries is a notable field mark." The dark phases of the two Rough-legs usually show a larger, less distinct, whitish area near the wing tips. Harris's Hawk has the basal half and the tip of the tail white, and it has chestnut patches on wings and thighs. A. H. Clark says that "in general actions and manner of flight the Black Hawk bears a strong resemblance to the Black Vulture, but it is almost never seen above the tree-tops; when it does soar, however, the similarity is very striking," but he adds that "the glaring white bands on the tail at once make it clear what bird it is."

FEEDING HABITS

The Mexican Black Hawk shows a varied taste in its feeding, eating frogs, snakes, lizards, fish, crustaceans, insects, small mammals and occasionally birds. G. N. Lawrence (1875) says that F. E. Sumichrast wrote of this species in southwestern Mexico, "I have taken out of their stomachs small quadrupeds, young birds, reptiles, crustacea, and insects. They are fond of fish and—easily catch the smaller kinds." Robert Ridgway (1885) says that one was seen in Yucatan eating a Currasow. E. A. Mearns (1886) says that "occasionally one was seen eating a fish" in Arizona. A. K. Fisher (1893) examined six stomachs: one held reptile remains; three, batrachians; two, fish; two, indeterminate matter. F. H. Fowler (1903) says that one in Arizona captured and ate a Green-tailed Towhee. A. H. Clark (1905) states that they are said to subsist entirely upon crabs, especially a fresh-water variety, in the Lesser Antilles. G. B. Thomas (1908) says that in British Honduras large land crabs form almost their entire food, but that they occasionally eat a lizard or snake, and he saw no indication that birds ever form part of their diet. Thomas Hallinan (1924) found the vertebrae of a small mammal in one stomach and crab fragments in three others from Panama. Allan Brooks (*in litt.*, 1931) found a

Grackle in the stomach of a bird from Texas, but states that it was almost certainly a poisoned bird.

Description—Length 20 to 23 inches, spread about 48 inches. Adult: Nearly uniform black or dark slaty, darker on wings, except tail which is crossed midway by a broad band of white and which also has white at the base and a narrow white tip; flight feathers mottled with rusty; a small whitish spot at the base of the primaries below; cere, legs and feet yellow. Immature: Upper parts brownish black streaked with rufous, buffy and white; under parts streaked with

MEXICAN BLACK HAWK
Ruled Area—Breeding Range

blackish, thighs heavily barred with same; "the contrast between cross-barred tibiae and lengthwise-striped breast and sides is always noticeable" (Coues); tail banded obliquely with about seven narrow black and white bars.

Range—"Lower Austral Zone in southern Arizona, and Texas (Lower Rio Grande Valley) south through Mexico and Central America to Peru and British Guiana." (A. O. U.)

A representative race occurs in the Lesser Antilles.

AMERICAN GOLDEN EAGLE

Adult on ground, immature in flight

THE EAGLES

Four species of Eagles have been recorded from North America, two being widely distributed permanent residents, one a resident of Greenland, and the fourth an accidental straggler from Asia. They are very large birds, only the California Condor exceeding them among our Raptors. They are birds of noble carriage and impressive power, much given to soaring at great elevations. When soaring, they can be recognized as Eagles at the limit of vision by their great expanse of broad wings in proportion to the length of their bodies, and by their conspicuous, fully feathered heads in contrast to the naked heads of the Vultures.

AMERICAN GOLDEN EAGLE

Aquila chrysaëtos canadensis (LINNAEUS)

Other Names. Ring-tailed Eagle, Mountain Eagle, Royal Eagle, Black, Gray or Brown Eagle.

As is the case with certain others of our Hawks, the economic status of the Golden Eagle varies with local conditions. In much of its present range this species is too rare to be considered as an important factor, and most certainly we should not permit its extermination, for it has an esthetic and scientific value which must not be forgotten. While this species undoubtedly kills wild game animals this is not a sufficiently serious matter to call for active interference by man. Because of its rarity in the United States and its diminution as a breeding species *it should be given complete protection* by law, except when individuals are destructive to domesticated animals, and control of such erring individuals should be placed in the hands of authorized game protectors, and not left to the general public.

The Golden Eagle is a haunter of remote mountain ranges, the Bald Eagle of forest-bordered lakes and of the seashore. This difference correlates with their feeding habits, the Golden Eagle being a hunter of wild game, rabbits, fawns, Grouse, and Waterfowl, while the Bald Eagle feeds very largely upon fish. The Bald Eagle usually nests in tall trees within the forest, the Golden Eagle sometimes builds in tall trees but more often on the inaccessible ledges of mountains.

When soaring the Golden Eagle holds its long blunt-ended wings almost perfectly level and straight, except the tips which are slightly upturned, while the Bald Eagle bends its wings more at the elbow when they are stiffly set. The light spot at the base of the primaries of the Golden Eagle is a good field mark, as is the white base and dark terminal band on the tail of the young bird. R. T. Peterson (1934) says the Golden Eagle when perched "appears flat-headed with a much smaller and less massive bill than the Bald Eagle." Both species progress, during straight ahead flight, by a succession of flappings and glidings, but the wing-beats of the Golden Eagle are quicker and more vigorous than those of the Bald Eagle and it is more graceful in flight. When prey is detected, the Golden Eagle some-times abruptly checks its flight and hovers for a moment with rapidly vibrating wings, like a gigantic Sparrow Hawk, before dropping like a plummet on its quarry. For such a large and heavy bird it shows surprising dexterity in catching Waterfowl and game birds. Its call has been given as *kau kau, kiah kiah kiah* or *kee kee kee*.

FEEDING HABITS

The Golden Eagle, as remarked above, is one of the few species of the diurnal birds of prey which can properly be accused of the destruction of game birds and mammals and of domesticated animals, but its rarity prevents its being a serious menace in most regions. J. J. Audubon (1831-1839) says it eats young fawns, raccoons, hares, Wild Turkeys, and other large birds, and carrion. C. E. Bendire (1892) lists in the food young fawns of antelope and deer, marmots, prairie dogs, hares, wood rats, squirrels and smaller mammals, Waterfowl from wild Geese to the smaller Ducks and waders, Grouse, and Sage Hens. E. S. Cameron (1905) says it feeds upon Sharp-tailed Grouse, jack rabbits, cottontails, mountain rats, Meadowlarks, and snakes, and later (1908) reports that a pair in Montana fed their young almost entirely upon prairie dogs and estimates that the family con-sumed about 636 of these destructive rodents during the nesting season. H. C. Oberholser (1906) says it eats fawns, sickly or weakened deer, young antelopes, mountain sheep, reindeer, mountain goats, foxes, raccoons, hares and rabbits, ground squirrels, tree squirrels, prairie dogs, marmots, pocket gophers, rats, wood rats, mice, lemmings, domestic animals, upland game birds of many kinds, Water-fowl, Shorebirds, a few larger Songbirds, reptiles, fish and carrion. Henninger and Jones (1909) state that in the West it feeds principally on small rodents and also upon lambs, shoats, fawns, game birds and poultry, snakes, etc., but that in the East poultry is taken more frequently and the young of domestic animals. I. N. Gabrielson (1922) says that two were found in Oregon feeding upon poisoned rabbits. A. Lano (1922) found a starving Eagle full of porcupine quills. E. L. Sumner, Jr. (1929) found remains of two snakes and of many rodents under a nest in California. W. C. Hanna (1930) examined remains of food about a nest in southern California and found that ground squirrels were the chief item with rabbits second in importance. D. A. Gilchrist (*mss.*, Bur. Biol. Surv.) found 39 skulls of prairie dogs, six cottontails and two ground squirrels at a nest in Arizona in 1916. W. E. Crouch (*mss.*, Bur. Biol. Surv.) observed Golden Eagles taking lambs in Idaho, and reports that Mrs. E. R. Yearin investigated a nest and found remains of 11 Sage Grouse, 13 ground squirrels, 7 rabbits, 5 lambs, and a King-fisher. H. B. McPherson (1910) says that at a nest of the Golden Eagle in Scotland the young bird was fed upon many rabbits and Grouse, a few hares and Ptarmigan, one brown rat and one small bird, while he was studying and photographing the bird.

Dr. A. K. Fisher (1893) states that "where rabbits, prairie dogs, or gophers are abundant, the Golden Eagle is very beneficial, confining its attentions mainly to these noxious animals; but in places where wild game is scarce it is often very destructive to the young of domesticated animals, and hence in such places has to be kept in check." W. C. Hanna (1930) felt that the bird was decidedly beneficial in southern California and "should receive our full protection"; he states that he has never seen "any first hand evidence that would indicate that Eagles destroy birds, poultry, or domestic animals."

RESULTS OF EXAMINATIONS OF STOMACHS AND CROPS

Authority	Number Examined	Mammals	Poultry or Game	Other Birds	Other Vertebrates	Insects	Miscellaneous	Empty
Fisher, A. K., 1893	6	2	0	1	0	0	2	1
Wayne, A. T., 1910	1	0	1	0	0	0	0	0
Bailey, B. H., 1918	5	1	0	1	1	1	0	2
Gloyd, H. K., 1925	30	31	0	2	0	0	0	0
Smith, J. D., *in litt.*, 1926	1	1	0	0	0	0	0	0
Miller, W. DeW., *mss.*, 1929	2	1	1	0	0	0	0	0
Brooks, Allan, *in litt.*, 1931	1	1	0	1	0	0	0	0
Bur. Biol. Surv., 1893-1931	28	20	3	1	0	0	3	2
Gloyd, H. K., *mss.*	3	2	1	0	0	0	0	0
Steen, M. O., *mss.*	1	1	0	0	0	0	0	0
Brimley, H. H., *mss.*	1	0	0	1	0	0	0	0
Wilson, Brownlow, *mss.*	1	0	1	0	0	0	0	0
Totals	80	60	7	7	1	1	5	5

Description—Length of male 30 to 35 inches, spread 75 to 84 inches; length of female 35 to 41 inches, spread 82 to 92 inches. Adult: Entire plumage dark brown, appearing almost black, except top of head and back of neck which are golden brown in marked contrast to the nearly black cheeks and chin; primaries and tail feathers black or dusky, with grayish or whitish areas at the base of the flight feathers which are noticeable in flight; the legs (tarsi) are feathered to the toes and are usually noticeably lighter colored than the rest of the under parts; the beak is bluish with yellow cere and the feet are yellow. Immature: Young birds just out of the nest are dark chocolate brown except for whitish areas on chin, lower throat or upper breast, and legs, and for irregularly scattered whitish feathers, and the tail, which shows its basal two-thirds white with a wide terminal band of blackish, this plumage being known as the "Ring-tailed Eagle." As the bird grows older the white on the tail and primaries diminishes, but it takes several years to acquire fully adult plumage.

AMERICAN
GOLDEN EAGLE
Ruled Area—Breeding Range
Black Area—Former Breeding Range
Dotted Line—Southern Boundary
of Winter Range

GRAY SEA EAGLE

Adult

Range—"Breeds in mountainous regions from northern Alaska, northwestern Mackenzie, and perhaps casually in the Canadian Provinces east of the Rocky Mountains south to northern Lower California, central Mexico, western Texas, Oklahoma, and formerly to North Carolina. Probably no longer breeds in the United States east of the Mississippi except possibly in North Carolina and eastern Tennessee. In winter south casually to Louisiana, Alabama, northern Florida, and southern Texas." (A. O. U.)

Representative races inhabit Europe, Asia, and northern Africa.

GRAY SEA EAGLE
Haliaeetus albicilla (LINNAEUS)

Other Names. White-tailed Sea Eagle, Erne.

This large Eagle is only an accidental straggler to North America outside of Greenland, and of course is of no economic significance. The adult should be easily recognized by its grayish head and white tail; young birds have the breast noticeably streaked with light and dark brown.

FEEDING HABITS

Henry Seebohm (1883) says that the food of the Gray Sea Eagle consists of "fish, sea fowl and occasionally carrion." A. Hagerup, according to Montague Chamberlain (1889), states that in Greenland it hunts Eider Ducks and sometimes preys upon Murres. W. H. Hudson (1895) gives its food as fish, mountain hares, lambs, Puffins, Guillemots, and other Waterfowl, Grouse and Ptarmigans, and carrion. Archibald Thorburn (1925) says it feeds largely on fish, rabbits and carrion, and that shepherds suffer from its depredations at lambing time. F. C. R. Jourdain wrote A. C. Bent (*mss.*, 1933) that Greenland birds subsist largely on fish, especially salmon, and on Brünnich's Murres, but it also eats Mallards, Eiders, Fulmars, Ptarmigan, and occasionally young seals.

Description—Length of male 31 to 36 inches, spread about 7 feet; length of female 35 to 40 inches, spread 7½ to 8 feet. Adult: Dark brown above and below, darkening on flight feathers; head and neck light brownish gray or grayish brown; tail white. Immature: Entire plumage much varied with shades of light and dark brown, giving streaked effect on breast; tail *not* white.

Range—"Breeds from northern Europe (formerly Scotland and Ireland) and northern Asia to Spitzbergen and to Novaya Zemlya; resident in Iceland and Greenland (breeding on west coast to Lat. 70° N.). In migration south to Japan, China, northern India, southern Europe and northern Africa. Casual in the Aleutian Islands—and recorded also from Cumberland Sound, —. Accidental off the coast of Massachusetts—." (A. O. U.) "Breeds freely in Roumania, Asia Minor, Northern Syria and Iraq.—It has never been recorded from Spitzbergen."(F. C. R. Jourdain, 1933.) Still breeds in Aland Island but is extirpated from Finland and Sweden. (Barnes, Ed., 1933).

THE EAGLES

AMERICAN or BALD EAGLES
Haliaeetus leucocephalus (Linnaeus)

Other Names. White-headed Eagle, White-tailed Eagle, Sea Eagle, Black Eagle, Gray Eagle, Bird of Washington, Old Abe, Bird-o'-freedom, Washington Eagle, Alaska Eagle.

Throughout much of its former range the Bald Eagle is today so rare and local as to be of little economic importance. In certain regions, like the coast of Florida, it is still fairly common, and on the coast of Alaska and British Columbia it may be called abundant in places. Its principal food is fish but in some localities it kills a good many water birds. It occasionally visits poultry yards in the more remote districts and picks up a few straggling chickens, and it also carries away wounded Ducks from under the very eye of the gunner. The Northern Bald Eagle is frequently accused of killing lambs, robbing fox farms, killing Ptarmigan and rabbits, eating salmon, and in other ways competing with its human rivals, especially in Alaska, where bounties amounting to many thousands of dollars have recently been paid for its scalp (or rather for its feet). The evidence on most of these counts is rather weak, except regarding the eating of salmon, and all the Bald Eagles in North America probably would have less effect on the salmon run than a single cannery, especially as many of the salmon eaten by the Eagles are dead or dying before the Eagles find them. Much of the destruction of fawns and of the young of domestic animals, for which the Bald Eagle is blamed, is undoubtedly the work of Golden Eagles. Dr. H. C. Oberholser (1906) sums up the situation by saying, "all things considered, the Bald Eagle is rather more beneficial than otherwise, since much of its food is of little or no direct economic value while the good it does more than compensates for its obnoxious deeds." On the other hand this magnificent appearing bird is an inspiration to all observers and of great esthetic interest, as it soars easily high overhead on wide-spread pinions, or perches, apparently in deep thought, on the jagged summit of some great dead tree beside the shore of a wooded lake or an inlet of the sea. As the Bald Eagle was adopted as an emblem of the United States on June 20, 1782, and is usually considered as our "National Bird," *it should be protected* for sentimental reasons regardless of its economic status. *Laws protecting it should be passed by every state in the Union and these should have the benefit of Federal enforcement.*

It is very unfortunate that the Bald Eagle, which is now rare over large parts of its former range, is often killed as a trophy, even in states where it is legally protected. A number of advertising taxidermists feature this bird on their catalogue covers to arouse interest in its being obtained as a mounted specimen. Frequent newspaper articles falsely accuse Eagles of attacking children and thus stir up unjustified popular prejudice against this mighty and interesting bird.

The Bald Eagle is a large and powerful but rather sluggish bird. Adults are easily recognizable, their white heads and tails being in marked contrast to their dark bodies. When perched in a tree, the white head of the adult Eagle against the dark background often attracts attention when otherwise the bird might be un-noticed. On the other hand, when soaring high overhead against a white cloud background, the head and tail may be practically invisible, only the dark body and long, broad wings showing. When startled from its perch, the bird launches for-ward with a spring that shakes the branches of the tree, and with powerful thrusts of its great wings it travels away with surprising speed. In straightaway flight the head, neck and body, while forming a straight line, are not horizontal but the head is raised above the level of the body and the bird "slopes down behind" in a char-acteristic posture. The wing strokes, while unhurried and rather labored, impress the observer with their power. The flight is quite different from that of the Great Blue Heron, which is frequently found in similar localities and which has nearly as great a wing spread as the Bald Eagle but whose wings in action seem very weak and "floppy." The Osprey approaches the Bald Eagle in size and in extent of wings, but its wings are narrower and more pointed, its upper parts are brown, its under parts largely unmarked white, and its tail is crossed with numerous bars of light and dark. The Bald Eagle frequently robs the Osprey, mounting above its victim and swooping down upon it and, as the Osprey loosens its hold and drops its prey, seizing the booty before it has dropped to the water or the ground. At such times the contrast between the two species is marked, both in form and action, but many people who see Ospreys describe them as "Eagles."

The immature Bald Eagle is often hard to distinguish from the Golden Eagle but the latter, if adult, will show golden brown on head and neck, and if imma-ture, will show the broad white basal portion of its tail with the black terminal band, while the tail of the young Bald Eagle is mottled with whitish, but not banded. The feathered tarsi of the Golden Eagle may sometimes be detected in the field as may the yellow legs of the Bald Eagle. When soaring at a great height colors are not plain and Eagles may be confused with Vultures under such condi-tions, but their silhouettes are distinctive, the former showing a wide expanse of broad, round-ended wings, a conspicuous feathered head, and a fan-shaped tail, while the Vultures have small naked heads; the Turkey Vulture has long but com-paratively narrow wings and its rather long tail is usually closed; the Black Vulture has proportionately short broad wings and a short tail which barely shows beyond the line of the wings. The Ferruginous Rough-leg and American Rough-leg in their dark phases resemble Eagles considerably, but here again the silhouettes are sufficient to distinguish them, their spread of wings being less in proportion to their body length than is the case with the Eagles.

FEEDING HABITS

The Bald Eagle feeds largely upon fish and carrion, varying its diet with birds, small mammals and reptiles. William Brewster (1880) says that on the Virginia coast they live principally upon Waterfowl, including Canada Geese and Brant and that he never knew them to catch fish though they frequently robbed Ospreys of their prey; later (1925) he states that in Maine they "subsist here largely on fish, chiefly large suckers and chubs, most of which, I suspect, are dead or dying and floating or swimming feebly on or near the surface." L. M. Turner (1886) says that in Alaska their food consists of Ptarmigan and sea birds. A. K. Fisher (1893) expresses it as his opinion that its favorite food is fish but that in the southern Atlantic states it feeds more upon Waterfowl and that this is also the case in Alaska and British Columbia. Outram Bangs (1898) says that in Florida it is a noted duck hunter but that in the North, as far as he knows, it never attempts to catch Waterfowl. Joseph Grinnell (1909) says that from October to April it feeds largely upon Waterfowl and fish on the Pacific coast; during migration it feeds largely upon Ducks but in May follows the schools of herring and later of salmon.

RESULTS OF EXAMINATIONS OF STOMACHS AND CROPS

Authority	Number Examined	Mammals	Poultry or Game	Other Birds	Other Vertebrates	Insects	Miscellaneous	Empty
Fisher, A. K., 1893	21	5	1	0	9	0	2	5
Bailey, B. H., 1918	4	2	1	0	0	0	0	1
Crabb, E. D., 1923	3	0	1	0	2	0	0	1
Smith, J. D., in litt., 1926 . .	1	0	0	0	1	0	1	0
Miller, W. DeW., mss., 1929	3	0	3	0	0	0	0	0
Brooks, Allan, in litt., 1931 .	2	0	1	0	0	0	0	0
Bur. Biol. Surv., 1893-1931 .	46	2	5	0	23	0	12	4
Totals	80	9	12	0	35	0	15	11

A. T. Wayne (1910) says that in the southern states it feeds largely upon fish and Ducks during the breeding season. George Willett (1914) says that in Alaska several dead Eagles were gorged with fawn meat and that their claws were covered with hair (but this may have been carrion); a nest he examined contained remains of Puffins and young Glaucous-winged Gulls. J. J. Van Kammen (1916) found about nests in Alaska, remains of Puffins, Auklets, Murres, Murrelets, Guillemots, Ducks, several species of waders, Longspurs, Rosy Finches, and Savannah Fox and Song Sparrows. Allan Brooks (1922) says that during most of the winter months and up to June or even July, Ducks and other Waterfowl form the bulk of their food but says that crabs may form a considerable part of the diet in summer, augmenting the fish which predominate then. F. H. Herrick (1924) studied the food brought to a nest in Ohio and states that fish formed 70% of the food of the young in 1922 and 96% of it in 1923. A. H. Howell (1924) says that Dr. Ralph found thirteen Coots under a nest and later (1932) relates that Alexander Wetmore found remains of three Cormorants, ten Ducks, one Tern, one Gull, one Wild Turkey, and ten fish, in refuse under two nests, and that D. J. Nicholson found remains of six species of birds, a rabbit, six fishes and a turtle, under other nests, all in Florida. E. H. Forbush (1927) says that they eat mammals from the size of a rat to that of a fox but that they rarely kill birds in New England. Allan Brooks (1929) examined numerous pellets from British Columbia and states that practically all of them were solid masses of Grebe feathers with only a few small bones; one contained the bill of a Duck. Herrick (1934) records that while studying a nest in Ohio, food was brought to the young one hundred and five times: "the food delivered consisted of eighty-seven fish (certified, seventy-nine; inferred, eight), thirteen chickens (certified, eight; inferred, five), and a smaller bird, possibly a plover. Among the fish, which were of various sizes up to a possible weight of four pounds, we recognized the lake and common catfish, sheepshead, sand and blue pike, carp and yellow perch, the cisco or herring, and probably the wall-eyed pike and white-fish, all representing the most abundant food fishes of Lake Erie. Later there were one or two large gold-fishes and a number of cusk or lake-lawyers."

The Bald Eagle has been described in two geographical races, but they are indistinguishable in the field.

NORTHERN BALD EAGLE
Haliaeetus leucocephalus alascanus C. H. Townsend

Description—Length about 34 to 43 inches, spread from 82 to 98 inches. Adult: Head, neck, tail, and tail coverts, white; rest of plumage brownish black; bill, cere, unfeathered part of legs, and feet, yellow. Immature: Often noticeably larger than the adults; nearly uniform grayish or brownish black, more or less mottled with whitish spots, principally on the under parts, wing coverts, and tail; at a distance they look dull black though not as black as a Vulture. As the young approach maturity, toward their third or fourth year, more white shows on the under parts and tail and some time after the third year the head and tail become white.

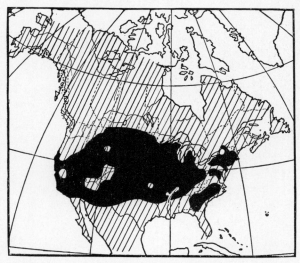

BALD EAGLES
Ruled Area—Breeding Range
Black Area—Former Breeding
Range

Range—"Boreal zones of northwestern Alaska, northern Mackenzie, and northern Quebec (Ungava) south to British Columbia and the Great Lakes. Winters south at least to Washington, Montana, and Connecticut." (A. O. U.)

SOUTHERN BALD EAGLE
Haliaeetus leucocephalus leucocephalus (Linnaeus)

Description—Length of male 30 to 34 inches, spread 72 to 85 inches; length of female 35 to 37 inches, spread 79 to 90 inches. This smaller race is indistinguishable in the field from its northern relative.

STELLER'S SEA EAGLE

Adult

Range—"United States to southern Lower California and central Mexico breeding in suitable locations throughout its range; rare and local in California (except in the Santa Barbara Islands) and in the arid interior states. Accidental in Sweden." (A. O. U.) Occasional in Bermuda (Bradlee).

STELLER'S SEA EAGLE
Thallasoaëtus pelagicus (PALLAS)

Other Names. White-shouldered Sea Eagle, Kamchatkan Sea Eagle.

This great bird when seen in flight can only be confused with the California Condor, both being dark birds with white areas at the front of the wings as seen from below, but the wedge-shaped tail of the Eagle is also white and its well feathered head is larger and darker. Elliott Coues (1903) remarked that this bird "no doubt sometimes flies across to the neighboring Aleutian Islands" from its Asiatic haunts and this prediction was justified when a single specimen was killed on St. Paul Island in Bering Sea in 1917 as reported by G. D. Hanna (1920), and a second specimen was recorded by C. H. Gilbert (1922) as taken on Kodiak Island, Alaska, in 1921.

Little is known definitely of the feeding habits of this species but it probably feeds largely upon fish, varied with sea birds. Baird, Cassin and Lawrence (1858) say, "it is strictly a fishing eagle, mainly deriving its subsistence from the sea, but occasionally capturing birds and quadrupeds."

A bird which has only been recorded twice in North America is naturally negligible as an economic factor, and there seems to be no reason for withholding protection.

Description—Length about 42 to 45 inches, spread 7 to 8 feet. Tail wedge-shaped, of fourteen feathers. Adult: Dark brown; forehead, most of wing coverts, rump, tail and thighs, white. Immature: Generally darker than adult; white parts more or less dusky.

Range—"Northeastern Siberia, Kamchatka, Sakhalin and Bering Islands. Casual on the Pribilof Islands and on Kodiak Island. South in winter to Chosen (Korea), Japan, and the Riu Kiu Islands." (A. O. U.)

MARSH HAWK

Adult male flying at left, adult female flying at right, immature perched.

THE HARRIERS

The only representative of this group in North America is the Marsh Hawk, widely distributed as a breeding bird from northwestern Alaska to Texas and Virginia. It is very closely related to the Harriers of Europe and Asia, in fact J. L. Peters (1931) considers our bird a subspecies of the European Hen Harrier under the subspecific name *Circus cyaneus hudsonius* (LINNÉ). Harriers somewhat resemble Falcons with their long, narrow wings but they lack the dashing flight which characterizes the Falcons.

MARSH HAWK
Circus hudsonius (LINNAEUS)

Other Names. Harrier, Marsh Harrier, Bog-trotter, Bog Hawk, Frog Hawk, Mouse Hawk, Snake Hawk, Rabbit Hawk, Mole Hawk, Mouser, Blue Hawk, White-rumped Hawk.

The Marsh Hawk or Harrier is a species whose feeding habits vary greatly in different places and at different seasons of the year, hence its economic status is subject to considerable difference of opinion. When rodents are plentiful the Harrier seems to prefer them to birds as an article of diet, as is very clearly shown in Stoddard's report from Georgia and Errington's from Wisconsin, given below, and it is at such times decidedly beneficial as Man's ally in controlling these destructive pests. In western Canada, where breeding Waterfowl abound and where small rodents may be scarce or less easy to obtain, the Marsh Hawk may be an objectionable species during the breeding season. Local conditions must establish the status of the bird and the question of its control or protection, but in most places *it is probably more beneficial than harmful*, it has considerable esthetic value, and it therefore should be protected except when actually detected in the act of committing depredations. Control measures, when permitted, should be in the hands of properly qualified game protectors and not in the hands of the general public; the closely related European Hen Harrier is today extinct or nearly so in the British Isles through the misdirected energies of prejudiced and uninformed game keepers.

The Harrier's flight is usually slow and indirect, with deliberate wing-beats and frequent skimming low over the ground, and is strongly suggestive of that of a sea gull. In the air it is a rather large appearing bird, due to its long wings and tail and the looseness of its body feathers, but in the hand "the smallness of its body and the lightness of its construction are evident" (Taverner). It floats about with an appearance of laziness or indifference, slowly flapping its long wings a few times and then sailing a short distance and repeating. When sailing, the wings are carried well above the plane of the body, forming an angle of about 120°, and the long primaries are seen to be spread like open fingers. The white rump sometimes gives an effect of the tail being separated from the body. The Harrier seldom alights on trees though it frequently perches on stumps or low posts from which it watches for its lowly prey.

The Harrier is most often seen zigzagging low over wet marshes and swamps and it almost never mounts high in air to circle or sail like the Red-tail or Red-shoulder, except during the courting season. The courtship evolutions are thus described by Norman Criddle (1912),—"He usually starts with a sort of wobbly flight as if imitating a tipsy individual, then swooping downwards, he turns completely over, occasionally several times in succession, and then darts up again, with a cackle, to repeat the same performance over again, often tumbling within a few feet of the female which is usually flying below. Occasionally these performances are terminated with the wobbly flight over again, at other times they neither start nor end in this manner. I have also observed the female try her skill in the same way but she lacks the confidence and grace of her husband."

The rather long pointed wings, long squarish tail, conspicuous white rump, facial disc, and characteristic low coursing flight make the Marsh Hawk one of our most easily recognized Hawks. The Everglade Kite somewhat resembles the Harrier in general coloration, deliberate flight, and fondness for extensive marsh-lands, but the Kite is darker, its wings are broader and its tail shorter in proportion, the base of the tail is white instead of the rump only, and its habitat in the United States is limited to certain parts of the peninsula of Florida. The ashy gray back of the White-tailed Kite suggests the adult male Harrier, but its white, unbarred tail and black shoulder patches are unmistakable. Swainson's Hawk in some plumages resembles the female or immature Marsh Hawk at a distance but its wings are broader and its tail shorter in proportion and its wings are carried nearly level when sailing, not at an angle above the body; at times the white patches at the sides of the rump of Swainson's Hawk suggest the white rump of the Harrier but they do not meet across the back. The American Rough-leg in its light phases sometimes suggests the Harrier by its low coursing flight, but it is a much heavier appearing bird, with broader wings, and usually shows a wide black abdominal band and prominent "wrist-mark." The long, narrow wings of the Harrier are somewhat falcon-like in outline but its actions are very unlike those of a typical Falcon, being slow and deliberate while the Falcon is speed and impetuosity personified.

The Marsh Hawk's nest is usually made upon the ground among bushes or tall growths in swampy places. The birds are often very noisy and threatening when the nest is approached. Their notes have been variously described as "a shrill squealing *quee-quee-quee*"; "a dry cackling *kep-kep-kep-kep*"; "complaining screams *cac-cac-cac-cac-cac* or *geg-geg-geg*"; "screeching notes."

88

FEEDING HABITS

The diet of the Marsh Hawk is quite varied though, as it is a very light and rather weak bird for its apparent bulk, it seldom attacks birds or mammals of any size unless they are wounded or sick. J. J. Audubon (1831-1839) says this species eats insects, especially crickets, small lizards, frogs, snakes, birds, and "it will attack partridges, plovers, and even Green-winged Teal when urged by an excessive hunger." Robert Ridgway (1877) says that stomachs of birds taken in Nevada were stuffed with lizards and held no other food. A. K. Fisher (1893) says, "its food consists largely of small rodents, such as meadow mice, half-grown squirrels, rabbits and spermophiles or ground squirrels—in addition it preys upon lizards, frogs, snakes, insects, and birds; of the latter, small ground-dwelling species are usually taken. When hard pressed it is said to feed upon offal and carrion.—It occasionally preys upon dead or wounded ducks left by gunners." A. L. and H. L. Ferguson (1922) recorded that of a large series killed at Fisher's Island, New York, 44% held mammals and 90% birds; the fact that this island is a game preserve and that the Hawks were practically all killed while migrating across Long Island Sound accompanied in their flight by many species of small birds, should be considered in weighing this evidence, however (details of this study are included in the table given below). L. A. Luttringer, Jr., (1930) examined a small series from Pennsylvania and found meadow mice in seven and a red squirrel in one, but no remains of birds. L. L. Snyder (1932) examined 27 stomachs from southern Ontario; rodents formed 39% of the food, poultry 7.2%, other birds 49.8%, amphibians 4%; two were empty. It is interesting to note that of these Ontario Marsh Hawks, ten were killed near the well-known bird sanctuary of Mr. Jack Miner and that all of these contained bird remains, but Mr. Miner used small birds as lures in decoying these Hawks, so that it was hardly a fair test of the Harrier's preferences as between mammal and avian food.

H. L. Stoddard (1931) collected 1098 pellets at a Marsh Hawk roost on a game preserve in Georgia: 925, or 84%, held remains of cotton rats, which Mr. Stoddard's studies have shown to be extremely destructive to nesting Quail; eight other species of mammals were identified; 138, or 12.6%, held remains of 36 species of birds, including however only four Bob-whites; 15 held snakes; 15, insects; in another lot of 177 pellets, 109, or 61%, held cotton rats and only one contained Quail remains. P. L. Errington (in litt., 1930) examined food material retrieved from adults or forced from the gullets of juveniles and found the remains of 175 rodents (including 104 meadow mice and 56 ground squirrels or chipmunks), two shrews, fifteen small birds, two snakes and ten frogs; he writes, "I consider the above items in the proportion listed as an accurate cross-section of the Marsh Hawk's food during the summer months" in the region studied, south-central Wisconsin, in 1929 and 1930. From remains about nests in New Jersey it was evident that "mice, and small birds, supplemented with insects, constitute the principal fare during early life" according to C. A. Urner (1925) who adds that "as the birds grow, rats assume a more important role." Norman Criddle (1912) says, "the parents are careful to pluck or skin everything before offering it" to their young, in Manitoba, and adds that the young birds "from August till the middle of September—are one of the worst enemies our Prairie Chickens have to contend with." As they become older they devote themselves to smaller and more easily captured prey, rodents and small birds. It seems probable that most of the destruction of poultry and small birds is either the work of Harriers in their first year or by adults who are feeding their young. J. A. Munro (1929) says that "at times rodents appear exclusively to engage the attentions of Marsh Hawks" in British Columbia and Alberta, but Allan Brooks (1928) calls this species "the most destructive hawk in America to our marsh-nesting water fowl for at least three months of the year."

RESULTS OF EXAMINATIONS OF STOMACHS AND CROPS

Authority	Number Examined	Mam-mals	Poultry or Game	Other Birds	Other Vertebrates	Insects	Miscel-laneous	Empty
Warren, B. H., 1890	14	8	0	3	3	2	0	0
Fisher, A. K., 1893	124	79	7	34	9	0	1	8
Bailey, B. H., 1918	7	5	1	2	0	1	0	1
Ferguson, A. L. & H. L., 1922	119	52	?	107	14	8	0	0
Miller, W. DeW., mss., 1929	15	14	0	5	0	0	0	2
Munro, J. A., 1929	3	2	0	1	0	0	0	0
Snyder, L. L., 1932	27	10	2	12	1	0	0	2
Pearson, T. G., 1933-b . . .	109	89	0	12	0	0	0	13
Totals	418	259	10	176	27	11	1	26

E. S. Cameron (1907) considers the Marsh Hawk "the most pertinacious of any in its attacks on the poultry yard" in Montana. H. K. Coale (1925) states that one bird killed seven of a flock of fourteen Hungarian Partridges in two weeks in Illinois. E. H. Forbush (1927) says, "they are considered great poultry pests on Martha's Vineyard," Massachusetts. On the other hand E. R. Kalmbach (1927) describes the services of these birds in frightening away rice-eating birds on a rice plantation in North Carolina "that could not have been hired by the owner for less than $300.00."

MARSH HAWK
Ruled Area—Breeding Range
Dotted Lines—Boundaries of
Winter Range

Description—Length of male 17.5 to 20 inches, spread 40 to 45 inches; length of female 19 to 24 inches, spread 43.5 to 54 inches. The sexes differ in color but in all plumages the species is distinguished by a conspicuous white patch on the back just above the tail (the rump). A ruff of feathers about the eyes suggests the facial disc of certain Owls. Adult male: Pale bluish or ashy gray above;

white below with a few rufous markings and with a grayish throat; tips of flight feathers black, especially prominent on primaries; tail gray with several dark bars. Adult female: Brown above, brightest on shoulders; a lighter somewhat streaked brown below; tail plainly barred with dark brown and buffy or creamy. Immature: Similar to female but face darker and under parts less streaked and more rufous.

Range—"Breeds from northwestern Alaska, northwestern Mackenzie, northern Manitoba, northern Ontario, central Quebec, and Newfoundland south to northern Lower California, southern Arizona, southern Texas, southern Illinois, southern Indiana, Ohio, Maryland, and southeastern Virginia. Winters from southern British Columbia, western Montana, western South Dakota, southern Wisconsin, southern Michigan, southern New York, southern Vermont, and southern New Hampshire south to the Bahamas, Florida, Cuba, and Colombia. Accidental in Hawaii and Barbados." (A. O. U.) Regular visitant in Bermuda (Bradlee).

AMERICAN OSPREY

Adults

THE OSPREYS OR FISH HAWKS

Ospreys are highly specialized fish-eating Hawks, the subfamily *Pandioninae* consisting of but a single species, *Pandion haliaëtus* of Linnaeus, which includes five subspecies, widely distributed over much of the known world. They are characterized by a peculiar firm close plumage, long wings, long legs (for a Hawk), and large strong toes which are covered with rough reticulate processes which apparently assist in holding their slippery prey. They also have a reversible outer toe so that when they grasp a fish the talons are paired, the better to hold it.

AMERICAN OSPREY
Pandion haliaëtus carolinensis (GMELIN)

Other Names. Fish Hawk, Sea Hawk, Fish Eagle, Fishing Eagle.

The Osprey is generally considered as harmless. In some places, as at Cape May, New Jersey; Gardiner's Island, New York; and Bristol County, Massachusetts; where it breeds in considerable numbers, it is protected by public sentiment as well as by law. In many other large areas, where it was formerly common in the breeding season, it is today much reduced in numbers, and unless some means can be found to prevent the heedless killing of these fine creatures, their continued decrease cannot be prevented.

Most of the fish taken by the Osprey are of species of little or no value for human consumption or sport, though Townsend and Bent (1910) state that it takes salmon and trout in Labrador, and in Yellowstone National Park, where Ospreys abound and are a much appreciated addition to the attractions of that great public recreation ground, trout are almost the only fish to be obtained. However, we can well spare a few fish now and then to keep these beautiful birds as an inspiring sight and an integral part of our wild landscape. The Osprey should be given complete protection at all times, except possibly about fish rearing establishments, where control by properly authorized persons may occasionally be permissible. Before control permits are given in such instances, efforts should be made by means of "scarecrows" and other devices, to protect the fish, without making it necessary to kill the Ospreys.

The Osprey is a bird of the seashore, lakes and rivers, and is seldom found far from large bodies of water. Even in migration this trait persists and it usually follows river valleys and the seashore in its annual journeys. It is a sociable bird, for a Raptor, and occasionally nests in straggling groups of considerable size when unmolested. It is almost exclusively a fish-eater and its manner of fishing is well known, flapping along deliberately thirty to a hundred feet above the water scanning the surface for its finny prey. When a fish is sighted, the Osprey may dive at once or it may hover for a moment with rapidly beating wings, then closing them, drop like a plummet into the water, where it may disappear completely from sight before emerging with its booty. When carrying a fish the Osprey almost invariably holds it with both feet in such a way that the head points forward and a minimum of air resistance is encountered. After a dive, the bird flies a short distance and then shakes itself all over like a water-soaked dog, the spray flying in all directions, the bird then continuing its flight.

The Osprey may usually be easily recognized because of its size, its plain brown upper parts, white under parts, distinctively marked head, and long and rather narrow wings. It approaches the Bald Eagle and Turkey Vulture in spread of wings and exceeds the Black Vulture and all the Buteos. Though often mistaken for an Eagle by the uninformed, it should be distinguished without difficulty by its white under parts. It can be distinguished from any of the Buteos by its silhouette, which shows long, narrow wings usually bent in a characteristic "crooked" outline, and a fairly long tail which is often spread fan-like when in flight. The tail is narrowly barred, and the head markings are distinctive.

The Osprey generally lives in peace and accord with other birds though it is reputed to drive all other Hawks away from its nesting grounds. It is well known that small birds like Grackles frequently build their nests in the interstices of the bulky homes of the Ospreys.

The common notes of the Osprey are surprisingly weak for such a large bird, and are almost exactly like the peeping of small chickens.

FEEDING HABITS

Only rarely does the Osprey deviate from a diet of fish, as is shown both by field studies and stomach examinations. T. G. Gentry (1877) states that "the food of this species consists mainly of fish, although the reptiles and frogs which infest the swamps where it builds, do not escape its vigilance." C. S. Allen (1892) found the wing of a freshly killed Crow in a nest containing young Ospreys on Plum Island, New York, and states that Night Herons in a nearby rookery were killed almost daily by the Ospreys which "seemed to unjustly accuse the herons of the robbery" of eggs by marauding Crows, but he had no positive evidence that either species was used *as food* by the Fish Hawks. C. E. Bendire (1892) says the food consists entirely of fish, usually of inferior quality; in Florida it is almost all catfish and near the Pacific coast it is to a great extent suckers. A. K. Fisher (1893) also states that the Osprey feeds entirely on fish. Paul Bartsch (1900) says, "I have often noticed one—with a water snake in its talons." C. G. Abbott (1911) quotes R. C. Murphy as having examined an Osprey "in a starved and emaciated condition" which had been killed with a stick by a woman who "had found the hawk with its talons sunk in a hen and flapping violently in an attempt to fly off with its prey." O. H. P. Rodman (1926) avers that he has known Ospreys to kill chickens on a few occasions but gives no definite data to back up the rather loose expression. C. D. Kuser (1929) states that a gamekeeper in New Jersey saw an Osprey swoop down and seize a young Duck and the following day the Osprey returned "and snatched up a half-grown Mallard," the Osprey being shot while carrying its prey. L. A. Luttringer, Jr. (1930), says that one was shot in Pennsylvania when it attempted to carry off a chicken. This constitutes all the evidence I have been able to find regarding any food of the Osprey other than fish.

Description—Length 21 to 24.5 inches, spread 54 to 72 inches. Adult: Above dark brown, crown more or less streaked with black; a broad blackish stripe through the eye and down the side of the neck; white superciliary line; rest of head, neck and under parts chiefly white, breast more or less streaked or spotted with dark brown, especially in female; flight feathers barred on under surface and with black tips; usually a conspicuous "wrist-mark"; tail with numerous bars and a narrow white tip; cere, legs and feet bluish. Immature: Similar but with white edges to many feathers of the upper parts, more or less buffy below, and tail more profusely barred.

AMERICAN OSPREY
Ruled Area—Breeding Range
Dotted Lines—Boundaries of
Winter Range

Range—"Breeds from northwestern Alaska, northwestern Mackenzie, Churchill, Hudson Bay, northern Manitoba, central Quebec, southern Labrador, and Newfoundland south to Lower California, western Mexico, the Gulf States, and the Florida Keys. Winters from Florida and the Gulf States, through Lower California and Mexico to the West Indies and Central America. Casual south to Peru, Chile, and Paraguay and north to Greenland." (A. O. U.) Occasional in Bermuda (Bradlee).

AUDUBON'S CARACARA

Adults in foreground and flying, immature in background

THE CARACARAS

The Caracaras are peculiar looking birds, closely related anatomically to the true Falcons, but very unlike them in external appearance and in habits, being much more like Vultures in many ways. They are long-legged birds, chiefly terrestrial, rather sluggish in action, and largely carrion-eaters. They are southern in distribution.

AUDUBON'S CARACARA

Polyborus cheriway auduboni CASSIN

Other Names. Caracara Eagle, Mexican Eagle, Mexican Buzzard, King of the Buzzards, Black-capped Eagle.

As a carrion eater and general scavenger *the Caracara deserves complete protection*, while the small animals of beneficial habits which it occasionally devours are balanced by the injurious species, such as rodents and poisonous snakes, which it also destroys.

The Caracara is a bird of the open country, seldom being seen in heavily wooded areas and preferring prairie regions, with mesquite thickets and scattered small trees in which it nests. Its appearance is striking and characteristic. Its straightaway flight is often sluggish appearing, with alternate flappings and sailings, but at times it is strong, rapid and direct. It frequently skims low over the ground and at other times circles high overhead. When perched, it holds itself very erect "with a strange grandfatherly appearance." While most Hawks hop, the Caracara walks and with its rather long legs *runs* with considerable speed. When emitting the "high cackling cry" or "hoarse raucous call" from which it gets its name, the head is thrown back until it seems to rest upon the bird's shoulders.

Being a carrion feeder, the Caracara is often found associated with both the Black and Turkey Vultures, but it is easily distinguishable. On the ground, its longer legs and its habit of walking instead of hopping, differentiate it from other Hawks even before its characteristic colors can be seen. In flight, its long straight wings with widely separated primaries, rather long tail, stiffly outstretched neck, and its conspicuous whitish areas on neck and breast, near tips of wings, on upper and lower tail coverts, and base of tail, make an unmistakable picture. "The bare face and great yellow beak with carmine base, forming a continuous curve with the forehead, are notably unique features," according to B. H. Christy.

FEEDING HABITS

The Caracara is primarily a carrion feeder but varies its diet with small creatures which it captures alive. J. J. Audubon (1831–1839) says it walks about in search of food and now and then picks up a frog or young alligator, in Florida. S. F. Baird (1859) says it destroys large numbers of the Texas field rat. G. B. Sennett (1879) examined three half-grown young which had been fed upon field mice. William Lloyd (1887) says that it feeds on carrion but also catches live fish and frogs and he has seen them in couples hunting prairie dogs. C. E. Bendire (1892) states that besides rabbits and small rodents it eats lizards, snakes, beetles, and grasshoppers, and he quotes Capt. B. F. Goss who states that on the coast of Texas he saw Caracaras robbing Brown Pelicans of their prey. A. K. Fisher (1893) says it eats carrion and offal, lizards, snakes, frogs, young alligators, crabs, crawfish, insects, young birds and mammals. He examined only two stomachs: one held carrion and maggots, the other held mammal remains. A. H. W. Norton (1896) says it eats field rats, snakes, lizards and rabbits, beetles and bugs. Mrs. F. M. Bailey (1902) says it eats carrion, mice, fish, and snakes. A. E. Schutze (1904) says that the cottontail rabbit forms about one-half of its diet in southeastern Texas, while A. P. Smith (1910) states that fish form the greater part of its food on the lower Rio Grande. Thomas Barbour (1923) says that he has often seen Caracaras chase large birds and that "Gundlach once saw one chase, tire and kill a White Ibis." D. J. Nicholson (1928) says, "their principal food is small turtles—rabbits are also a favorite." Since 1893 the Bureau of Biological Survey has examined a few stomachs, five of which held squirrels or rabbits; one, feathers; five, reptiles or amphibians; one, insect larvae; three, carrion.

Description—Length 20 to 25 inches, spread about 48 inches. Adult: Face bare, bright red to yellow; head slightly crested; crown black; back, wings, and belly rusty black; throat dingy white or buffy; nape and breast barred black and buffy; wings blackish but with a conspicuous whitish

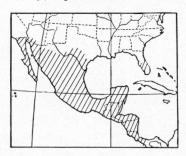

AUDUBON'S
CARACARA
Ruled Area—Breeding Range

area at base of primaries; upper and lower tail coverts white; tail white with numerous narrow black bars and a broad blackish terminal band; bill large, horn color; feet and tarsus yellow. Immature: Plumage more brown; breast, etc., streaked more than barred; tail as in adult.

Range—"Northern Lower California, southwestern Arizona, Texas, and Florida south through Mexico and Central America. Accidental in Ontario." (A. O. U.)

Representative races are found in the Tres Marías Islands off the west coast of Mexico, and from Panama to Peru and the Guianas.

GUADALUPE CARACARA

Polyborus lutosus RIDGWAY

As this species was formerly found only on Guadalupe Island off the coast of Lower California and is now undoubtedly extinct, detailed description is unnecessary. It was a paler and browner bird than the Audubon's Caracara and nearly the entire plumage was barred. It probably differed but little in habits from the latter species but our knowledge of the bird is very limited. Dr. Edward Palmer (1876), who first described the Guadalupe Caracara, stated that it ate small birds, mice, shellfish, worms, and insects, and that it was considered a great enemy of poultry and domestic animals, especially lambs and kids. This latter fact, coupled with its extremely limited range, contributed principally to its extinction at the hands of Man. *Its fate should be a warning to us to protect other diminishing species before it is too late.*

WHITE GYRFALCON

Adult on ground, immature in flight

THE FALCONS

The true Falcons are characterized by their long narrow pointed wings, fairly long tails, rather large heads, powerful bodies, and dashing flight. They are mostly birds of wild or sparsely settled country by choice, though the Sparrow Hawk has taken very kindly to city life and the Duck Hawk still breeds within sight of New York City and often winters in large cities like Boston, Washington and Chicago, where it feeds upon domestic pigeons, Starlings and House Sparrows. Except for the handsome little Sparrow Hawk, they are largely bird killers, but they are not common enough to call for restrictive measures and indeed should be protected unless actually engaged in raiding poultry or game farms.

GYRFALCONS
Falco rusticolus LINNEAUS

While the beautiful great Gyrfalcons are undoubtedly destructive in rookeries of water birds in their northern breeding grounds, they are too rare to be considered from a purely economic point of view when present in the United States or southern Canada, and *they should be protected for their esthetic value*, unless persistently engaged in depredations about farms. This is one of the instances where the "bird lover" and the gunner may disagree, but the former's right to the enjoyment of a glimpse of this rare and interesting species should receive as much consideration as the latter's fear that it may, for its food, capture game birds or animals which the gunner himself wishes to kill.

The flight of the Gyrfalcon is characterized by rapid powerful strokes of its long pointed wings, interrupted at intervals by brief periods of straightforward sailing, something like that of the Goshawk, but the rounder ends of the broader wings of the latter bird should distinguish it. Kumlien describes the flight of the Gyrfalcon as much slower than that of the Duck Hawk, suggesting endurance rather than swiftness, while Audubon says it is "more elevated, majestic, and rapid." Major Brooks apparently reconciles these contradictory statements by saying, "the flight of this falcon is as a rule rather slow compared with that of other large falcons, but when in pursuit of a duck it gets up a tremendous velocity and can twist and turn almost as quickly as a Goshawk. In ordinary flight the wing stroke is shorter than a Peregrine's, and the bird when going straight away appears to be hovering like a Kestrel." Audubon thus describes the habits of the Gyrfalcon in Labrador—"they rarely sailed when traveling to and fro but used a constant beat of the wings—they would hover motionless—and—descend almost vertically on their unsuspecting victims—now and then they would alight on some of the high stakes—and stand for a few minutes, not erect like most other Hawks, but in the position of a *Lestris* or tern."

BLACK GYRFALCON

Adult perched, immature in flight

In their most southerly breeding region, the only possible confusion in identification would be with the smaller Duck Hawk, the American Rough-leg which has long round-ended wings, and the Goshawk which has shorter round-ended wings. Gyrfalcons are rather "featureless" in their lack of distinctive markings. The Duck Hawk resembles the Gyrfalcon in silhouette but it is usually much darker above and lighter by contrast below, and it has a blackish crown, moustache and cheek-patch, with a light throat; while the closely related Prairie Falcon of the West has a decidedly ashy or clay-colored appearance. The American Rough-leg resembles the Gyrfalcon in size only, being heavy bodied and sluggish in its movements. The Goshawk approaches the Gyrfalcon in size, and they are sometimes confused but their silhouettes should prevent mis-identification under good conditions for observation. The White Gyrfalcon shows some resemblance to the similarly colored Snowy Owl but it is not so bulky appearing, its head is smaller and its wings more pointed, and its flight is more rapid and direct.

The aeries of the Gyrfalcon are usually located on bare and inaccessible ledges of a cliff. Breeding in a generally treeless region, they rarely or never alight in trees even during their southern wanderings, preferring a crag or an exposed boulder for a perch.

FEEDING HABITS

There is very little definitely recorded regarding the food of the Gyrfalcon. J. J. Audubon (1840–1844) found remains of Murres, Puffins and Ptarmigan near a nest in Labrador, as well as pellets containing fur and bones: a stomach which he examined contained remains of fish, feathers and hair (but the fish may have been from the gullet of a bird). John Murdoch (1885) says they feed upon young wild

RESULTS OF EXAMINATIONS OF STOMACHS AND CROPS

Authority	Number Examined	Mammals	Poultry or Game	Other Birds	Other Vertebrates	Insects	Miscellaneous	Empty
Stejneger, Leonhard, 1885 . .	5	3	0	1	0	0	0	1
Chamberlain, Montague, 1889	1	0	1	0	0	0	0	0
Taylor, A. O'D., 1892 . . .	1	1	0	0	0	0	0	0
Fuller, A. B., 1922	1	0	1	0	0	0	0	0
Brooks, Allan, in litt., 1931 .	5	0	1	0	0	0	0	4
Sutton, G. M., 1932	4	1	0	1	0	0	0	2
Totals	17	5	3	2	0	0	0	7

fowl and Ptarmigan in the Point Barrow region. L. M. Turner (1886) says they feed principally upon lemmings. A. K. Fisher (1893) says that they feed upon hares, Ptarmigan, Grouse, Waterfowl, Shorebirds, and other mammals and birds of medium size. Donald MacMillan (1918) says that the White Gyrfalcon feeds upon Arctic hares, Ptarmigan, Eider Ducks, Guillemots, and Dovekies. Archibald Thorburn (1925) says their food consists principally of Ducks and other Waterfowl. Bernard Hantzch (1929) says that Ptarmigan are their favorite food but that they feed upon everything possible, including fox baits, etc. O. L. Austin, Jr. (1932), watched two pairs hunting over their breeding grounds in Newfoundland Labrador and found the region swarming with white-footed mice and Labrador voles but no other food animals.

Description—According to the fourth edition of the Check-List of the American Ornithologists' Union (1931) "the status of the Gyrfalcons is still undetermined," but three races of *Falco rusticolus* are credited to northern North America. Two other races are found in Iceland and northern Europe. As these birds are usually rare even in their Arctic breeding grounds and are only casual visitors in southern Canada and in the United States, detailed subspecific description is not necessary here.

Gyrfalcons are large Hawks of typical falconine outline. Length from 20 to 25 inches, spread 44 to 52 inches. They vary from nearly pure white or white spotted with brown or black, to brownish black or almost black. At the two extremes, there is but little contrast between the upper and lower parts, and there is complete absence of distinguishing marks like moustaches, "wrist-marks," etc. In the phase usually known as the Gray Gyrfalcon there is considerably more contrast between the dark upper parts and the lighter lower parts, which are barred and spotted in the adult and heavily streaked in the immature; the cere and feet are usually yellow in the adult and bluish in the immature birds.

WHITE GYRFALCON
Falco rusticolus candicans GMELIN

Other Names. White Hawk, Greenland Falcon, Winter Falcon, Gray Gyrfalcon, Winterer.

Range—"Resident in Greenland, eastern Arctic America (probably), Spitzbergen, and

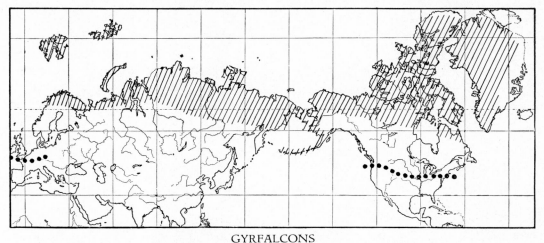

GYRFALCONS
Ruled Area—Breeding Range. Dotted Line—Southern Boundaries of Winter Range

Franz Josef Land (probably). Casual in winter south to British Columbia, Montana, Ontario, Quebec, Nova Scotia, Maine, and to the British Isles, France, and Germany" (A. O. U.). One record for New York (Griscom), Pennsylvania (Poole), Norway, Lapland, Murman Coast, Kanin Peninsula (Pleske).

ASIATIC GYRFALCON
Falco rusticolus uralensis SEWERTZOV and MENZBIER

Range—"Siberia to Kamchatka, islands in Bering Sea, and Bering Sea coast of Alaska. South, casually, in winter to Washington." (A. O. U.)

BLACK GYRFALCON
Falco rusticolus obsoletus GMELIN

Other Names. Labrador Gyrfalcon, Brown Gyrfalcon, Gray Gyrfalcon.

Range—"Northern North America from Point Barrow to Labrador. South in winter to Nova Scotia, Quebec, and Maine, casually to New York, New Hampshire, Massachusetts, Rhode Island, and Connecticut; also probably South Dakota, Kansas, Minnesota, Ohio, and Pennsylvania although some of these records doubtless represent the gray phase of *F. r. candicans*." (A. O. U.)

PRAIRIE FALCON
Falco mexicanus SCHLEGEL

Other Names. American Lanner Falcon, Lanneret (male).

The Prairie Falcon is one of our birds which, although found over a considerable area, is so restricted in its breeding sites and so commonly destroyed by hunters and sportsmen, that it is rapidly decreasing and has become so rare in large areas that its economic status is immaterial. It should be protected on the basis of its magnificent appearance and its rarity. Although at some times it apparently feeds almost entirely upon birds, at other times it destroys great quantities of injurious rodents like ground squirrels and gophers, and destructive insects like grasshoppers and crickets. Such a species should always be protected except when in the act of destroying property.

The Prairie Falcon is generally found haunting canyons and ridges in the more treeless portions of the western United States and southwestern Canada. It is often rather unsuspicious and allows fairly close approach when, perched on a telephone pole or fence post, it watches for its prey. Its flight, while swift, is usually low and it is not much given to soaring. N. S. Goss (1891) wrote of it, "in flight it progresses swiftly, by quick powerful strokes of its wings, often stopping in its flight to hover as it sights its prey beneath, descending upon the same with partly closed wings, swift as an arrow; or gives chase, turning and tacking easily and with a speed that the swiftest of fliers cannot escape." Major Brooks writes me, "the Prairie Falcon, while able to kill fast flying birds like ducks very prettily, is noteworthy (for a falcon) in its pursuit of small mammals like ground squirrels, marmots and jack rabbits. In striking at these, it descends like a bullet at a long low angle, and if the animal is missed it may ricochet along the ground for some distance, striking again and again, a puff of dust marking each unsuccessful effort."

PRAIRIE FALCON
Adult male

The Prairie Falcon resembles the Duck Hawk in size and actions, though it is not as courageous and "noble" as the latter. It is much lighter in color, with less contrast between the upper and lower parts, and with a less prominent "moustache." Both Falcons nest on ledges or in caves of cliffs but the Duck Hawk's aerie commonly overlooks water, while the Prairie Falcon frequently nests in very arid country. It is intermediate in speed between the Duck Hawk and the larger, slower Gyrfalcon. The Pigeon Hawk is smaller and decidedly darker than the Prairie Falcon. All the Falcons are easily distinguished from the Accipiters in flight by the quick hard strokes of their slender pointed wings.

When its nesting site is approached, the Prairie Falcon frequently gives a high pitched call, *kee kee kee*, and at other times a mellow quavering *wert-wert-wert-wert-wert*, a rattling *kr-r-r* or a peevish whining *kruk*.

FEEDING HABITS

The Prairie Falcon feeds principally on birds and mammals, with an occasional reptile or large insect. Robert Ridgway (1877) shot one which was feeding upon a large jackass rabbit, and reports seeing one catch a chicken and others chasing domestic pigeons and robbing Marsh Hawks of their prey. Henry Nehrling (1882) says, "its food is said to consist especially of Prairie Chickens and domestic fowl."

RESULTS OF EXAMINATIONS OF STOMACHS AND CROPS

Authority	Number Examined	Mammals	Poultry or Game	Other Birds	Other Vertebrates	Insects	Miscellaneous	Empty
Aughey, Samuel, 1878 . . .	1	0	1	0	0	1	0	0
Fisher, A. K., 1893	11	2	3	5	0	2	0	3
Bryant, H. C., 1918	1	1	0	0	0	0	0	0
Decker & Bowles, 1930 . . .	4	1	3	0	0	0	0	0
Brooks, Allan, *in litt.*, 1931 .	10	2	2	3	0	1	0	3
McLean, D. D., 1932	2	0	1	0	0	1	0	0
Bur. Biol. Surv., 1893-1931 . .	11	7	1	5	0	0	0	0
Totals	40	13	11	13	0	5	0	6

A. K. Fisher (1893) says it feeds upon "Prairie Hens, doves, blackbirds, and in fact any species" among birds and also upon "gophers, prairie dogs, rabbits and mice—lizards occasionally—large crickets and grasshoppers." E. S. Cameron (1907) adds Mallards, Teal, Sharp-tailed Grouse, and poultry. J. G. Tyler (1923) says that small birds are preferred at all times and only rarely does it take a mammal of any kind; about a nesting cliff he found quantities of feathers of Gambel's Sparrows, Western Meadowlarks, Valley Quail and Western Morning Doves, but the only mammal remnant was the foot of a rabbit "perhaps dropped by a Barn Owl nesting a few yards away"; at another nest, however, he found remains of a ground squirrel. S. G. Jewett (1926) saw one pursuing a female Ring-necked Pheasant and says that this bird "is sure a pheasant killer" on game farms. On the other hand,

P. A. Tavener (1926) says, "it on occasion turns seriously to grasshoppers." Decker and Bowles (1930) say its food in the nesting season consists almost entirely of cottontail rabbits and young jack rabbits, but three birds killed in winter in Washington held Meadowlarks while one from California held a Coot. F. H. Fowler (1931) collected pellets and fragments of food from three nests in California and found remains of twenty-six rodents and sixty-one birds.

Description—Length of male 17 to 18 inches, length of female 18.5 to 20 inches; spread about 40 to 42 inches. Adult: General color above brownish gray or clay color; an ill-defined whitish line over eye; cheeks whitish, with brown or black moustache; more or less whitish on nape, under parts whitish streaked or spotted with dark brown except on throat; tail, pale brown with narrow white tip and more or less distinct barring with whitish; feet and legs yellow. The whitish throat, cheeks and nape give the effect of an indistinct whitish collar and may serve as a distinguishing mark in the field under good conditions for observation, but the pallid, bleached appearance of the entire plumage is usually sufficient, coupled with its typical falconine outline. Immature: Upper parts a redder brown, under parts more heavily streaked on a more buffy ground; feet and legs bluish.

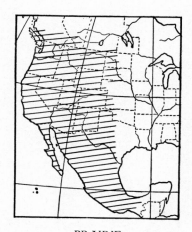

PRAIRIE
FALCON
Ruled Area—Breeding Range

Range—"Transition and Austral zones from the eastern border of the Great Plains and from British Columbia, southern Alberta, and southeastern Saskatchewan to southern Lower California and southern Mexico. Casual east to Manitoba, Minnesota, and Illinois." (A. O. U.)

PEREGRINES OR DUCK HAWKS
Falco peregrinus Tunstall

The Duck Hawk and Peale's Falcon are the American representatives of the Peregrine Falcons, the birds which in the days of Chivalry gave their name to the sport of Falconry. The larger female Peregrine was known as the "Falcon" and the smaller male as the "Tiercel," and only nobles of the rank of earls and higher were allowed to fly these "noble" birds.

The Duck Hawk, more than any other Hawk, would seem to deserve the approbation and admiration of the sportsman for its inherent qualities—speed, power and courage. According to G. H. Thayer (1904) the Duck Hawk "is, perhaps, the most highly specialized and superlatively well-developed flying organism on our planet today, combining in a marvelous degree the highest powers of speed and aerial adroitness with massive, warlike strength. A powerful, wild, majestic, independent bird, living on the choicest of clean, carnal food, plucked fresh from the air or the surface of the waters, rearing its young in the nooks of dangerous mountain cliffs, claiming all the atmosphere as its domain, and fearing neither beast that walks nor bird that flies, it is the very embodiment of noble rapacity and lonely freedom. It has its legitimate and important place in the great scheme of things, and by its extinction, if that should ever come, the whole world would be impoverished and dulled." William Brewster (1925) says of the Duck Hawk, "when the high-spirited Falcon is under full headway he cleaves the air with well-nigh meteoric velocity, lashing it ceaselessly with his narrow, shapely pinions. Although their peculiar vibrating or quivering motion seems almost effortless, it doubtless calls for much exertion on the part of the great pectoral muscles which originate it. From such a wing-driven projectile as a Duck Hawk moving thus, the birds he pursues, however swift-flying and resourceful, have no chance whatever of escape, except by doubling at the right moment, or by gaining sanctuary in dense cover."

The Duck Hawk was a favorite bird with my friend and mentor, the late Edward Howe Forbush, and he loved to watch it and to study its habits. In his last great book, "The Birds of Massachusetts and other New England States" (1927), he wrote, in part, "The favorite retreats of this Hawk are cliffs or crags overlooking some broad river valley with a stream meandering far below. It often watches from a dead tree on the steep mountainside, but more often patrols the valley at a considerable height or swings upward in wide circles until it reaches such an altitude that it is unseen or forgotten by its prospective victims. Its flight is one of the most wonderful exhibitions of speed and command of the air shown by any bird. At times, when heading into the wind, it will slide off sidewise covering a mile thus in a matter of seconds. It can so regulate its flight at will as seemingly to bound up-

DUCK HAWK

Adult on ground, immature in flight

ward for 100 or 200 feet like a flash, and apparently with the greatest ease. It can overtake and capture any of our birds in flight except possibly the Chimney Swift, and the only hope its victims have to elude it is by dodging its rushes, until they can dive into some tangle of vines and shrubbery. Fierce and audacious in pursuit of its victims, it does not hesitate to rush with incredible rapidity into the very farm-yards in pursuit of poultry or pigeons, and to strike down its terrified quarry in the near presence of its arch-enemy, Man.—From its mountain heights this hawk surveys the shining waters and the valleys spread below. Its piercing eye selects its prey in full flight, and it falls on its victim like a thunderbolt from the sky. It is the master of the air within its wide domain."

It is rather hard to blame the poultryman or game farmer for condemning the Duck Hawk, for its depredations are too well known to be overlooked. The sportsman has much less excuse for killing this fine species, however, for the Duck Hawk in capturing game birds and Waterfowl for food is only carrying out its instinct for self-preservation, while few gunners today really shoot *for food*, but only for the gratification of their lust for killing. P. A. Taverner (1926) says, "it is as wary as it is spirited, and rarely comes close to Man's residence or his poultry yards.—An accomplished killer of wild fowl, the Peregrine is a thorough sportsman in its hunting, and captures its prey by direct, irresistible attack, or straight pursuit, instead of crafty surprise, and, as a sportsman and a historical figure, can claim indulgence from human rivals. There should be enough game in the country to support so picturesque a character without arousing the jealousy of other hunters." Gerald Thayer (1904) says, "does it not seem as if a bird of such vast interest to the naturalists, the poets, and all literate persons and lovers of life in general, ought to be carefully preserved as an element of the intrinsic natural beauty of the country?"

The Duck Hawk's silhouette will quickly identify it from any other Raptors except the rare Gyrfalcon, the Prairie Falcon and the Pigeon Hawk. Its dark upper parts contrasting with its light under parts and its black crown, moustache and cheek, mark it easily from the larger and less contrasted Gyrfalcon if seen under reasonable observation conditions. The Prairie Falcon is much paler and more sand-colored or clay-colored both above and below. The Pigeon Hawk is considerably smaller than the Duck Hawk, the adult is paler bluish above and more heavily streaked below and the tail is more plainly banded, but the immatures are very much alike in markings except that the moustache of the Pigeon Hawk is less conspicuous.

FEEDING HABITS

The Duck Hawk is known throughout its range as a killer of birds, seldom deviating from this diet for small mammals or other prey. J. J. Audubon (1840–1844) says, "they occasionally feed upon dead fish that have floated to the shores and sand bars" of rivers, but this testimony is so different from that of other naturalists that one wonders if there is not some mistake in attributing this habit to the Peregrine. A. K. Fisher (1893) states that it feeds almost entirely upon birds "of which water fowl and shore birds form the greater part." C. E. Bendire (1892) quotes Charles Littlejohn as saying that Peale's Falcon takes great toll of Murrelets, Auklets, and similar water birds, which it hunts at some distance from land and eats near the place of their capture, hovering "stationary for several minutes at the time; in the meantime the prey is raised well up to the beak with both feet and promptly devoured." G. H. Thayer (1904) found feathers of domestic poultry and pigeons, Ruffed Grouse, Flickers, Blue Jays, Belted Kingfishers, Nighthawks, Robins, Sparrows, and other birds, near a nest in western Massachusetts. Allen and Knight (1913) found remains of Rough-winged Swallows, Meadowlarks, Flickers, Robins, Bluebirds, Goldfinches and many pigeons near a nest in New York State. V. F. Richards (1919) reports Blue Jays, Kingbirds, Nuthatches, Rose-breasted Grosbeaks, Scarlet Tanagers, Flickers, Mourning Doves, Phoebes, various Warblers and Sparrows, Veeries, and domestic pigeons and poultry, near another nest in Massachusetts. Several other observers testify that pigeons form a very large part of the food of this bird whenever it nests near Man's habitations, and the Duck Hawk also frequently spends the winter in cities like Boston, Washington, Chicago and San Francisco, where its diet is composed almost entirely, during its stay, of domestic pigeons, Starlings and House Sparrows, in which case it seems a decidedly desirable addition to the urban population. L. W. Smith (1921), however, states that the young in a nest in Connecticut were fed forty-four young Mallard Ducks from a nearby park pond. Edwin Beaupre (1922) examined pellets found near a nest in Canada which contained skulls and bones of meadow mice; nearby were two dead woodchucks and remains of Black Ducks, Green Herons, Florida Galli-nules, Killdeer, Ruffed Grouse, Nighthawk, Blue Jay, Black-billed Cuckoo, Mead-owlark, Kingfisher, Scarlet Tanager, Brown Thrasher, Flicker, and domestic fowl. I. N. Gabrielson (1922) saw one strike a Cinnamon Teal "traveling at a terrific rate of speed" and carry it away. P. A. Taverner (1926) says that Franklin's Gull is a favorite article of food in some of the Canadian prairie provinces, and that it captures Mallards and full-grown Ruffed Grouse on occasion. E. H. Forbush (1927) says that E. P. Bicknell once saw one capture a monarch butterfly, which, however, was dropped or allowed to escape, apparently uninjured; Mr. Forbush further states that birds from the size of Snow Buntings to the largest Ducks and Grouse are taken, domestic fowl occasionally, and pigeons very frequently, and he includes large insects like beetles and dragonflies in its diet; he says that he found feathers of Ring-necked Pheasants and Ruffed Grouse at nests, but "very few re-mains of mammals." S. J. Darcus (1930) says that Peale's Falcon feeds upon Ancient and Marbled Murrelets, Cassin's Auklets, and an occasional California Murre, near the Queen Charlotte Islands. G. M. Sutton (1932) saw a Duck Hawk kill a White-rumped Sandpiper at Southampton Island, Hudson Bay. A. C. Bent (mss., 1933) says that sea birds and Ptarmigan seem to form the main portion of the food of Peale's Falcon in the Aleutian Islands.

RESULTS OF EXAMINATIONS OF STOMACHS AND CROPS

Authority	Number Examined	Mammals	Poultry or Game	Other Birds	Other Vertebrates	Insects	Miscellaneous	Empty
Warren, B. H., 1890	3	0	1	0	0	0	0	2
Fisher, A. K., 1893	20	1	7	9	0	2	0	4
Worthington, W. W., 1899 .	1	0	0	0	0	1	0	0
Miller, W. DeW., mss., 1929.	21	1	3	15	0	4	0	3
Sutton, G. M., 1932	3	1	0	2	0	0	0	0
Pearson, T. G., 1933-a . . .	4	0	0	4	0	0	0	0
Bur. Biol. Surv., 1893-1931 . .	50	0	?	40	0	5	0	?
Totals	102	3	11	70	0	12	0	9

Three races of the Peregrine are included in the fourth edition of the Check-List of the American Ornithologists' Union and so are included in this volume, but F. C. R. Jourdain (1933) says that the European form *Falco peregrinus peregrinus* is included only on the basis of two specimens shot in East Greenland, one of which "closely resembled" the American form *Falco peregrinus anatum*, "while the other was more like the European race!" The Peregrine is a species of wide distribution in both the Eastern and Western Hemispheres, and J. L. Peters (1931) recognizes thirteen subspecies.

PEREGRINE FALCON
Falco peregrinus peregrinus TUNSTALL

Other Names. Peregrine, Falcon (female), Tiercel or Tassel (male).

Description—Similar to the Duck Hawk (which see below), but more heavily marked below and with the chest barred and spotted with brown or black.

Range—"Breeds from northern Siberia and Novaya Zemlya to the Pyrenees, Alps, and northern Italy, east to the Urals. Winters south to Africa and the Indian Peninsula. Casual in Greenland" (A. O. U.).

DUCK HAWK
Falco peregrinus anatum BONAPARTE

Other Names. American Peregrine Falcon, Great-footed Hawk, Ledge Hawk, Stone Hawk, Rock Hawk, Bullet Hawk.

Description—Length of male 15 to 18 inches, spread about 38 to 43 inches; length of female 18 to 20 inches, spread about 43 to 46 inches. Adult: Above dark bluish ash or slaty plumbeous with darker bands, lightest on rump and nearly black on head; top of head, cheeks, and prominent "moustache," blackish; under parts vary from white to creamy or buffy white or even pinkish buff, regularly barred on lower breast, belly, sides, etc., with blackish brown; throat and upper breast usually unmarked; tail with narrow white tip and about six narrow black bands and a broader subterminal band of black; bill horn color; cere, toes and tarsus yellow. Immature: Similar but upper parts brownish or blackish, feathers with rusty edges; under parts streaked with dark brown except on throat.

PEALE'S FALCON
Upper figures, adult female and immature

PEREGRINE FALCON
Lower figure, adult female

AMERICAN PEREGRINES
Ruled Area—Breeding Range
Dotted Lines—Boundaries of
Winter Range

Range—"Breeds locally from Norton Sound, Alaska, northern Mackenzie, Boothia Peninsula, Baffin Island, and the west coast of central Greenland south to central Lower California, central Mexico, Arizona, central western Texas, Kansas, Missouri, Indiana, Pennsylvania, and Connecticut, and in the mountains to Tennessee. Winters from Vancouver Island through California, and from Colorado, southeastern Nebraska, southern Illinois, Indiana, Pennsylvania, New Jersey, New York (Long Island), and Massachusetts to the West Indies and Panama. Casual in South America and accidental in Europe" (A. O. U.). Bermuda (Bradlee).

PEALE'S FALCON
Falco peregrinus pealei RIDGWAY

Description—Similar to *F. p. anatum* but much darker. Adult: Upper parts including head, dark slate; breast heavily spotted with blackish; belly, sides, etc., with broad, dusky bars. Immature: Upper parts lack rusty edges to feathers; lower parts sooty blackish streaked with pale buff.

Range—"Breeds on the Queen Charlotte (?), Aleutian, and Commander Islands. Transient in the Sitkan district, Alaska. South in winter to Oregon." (A. O. U.)

Other races of *Falco peregrinus* in Europe Asia, Malaysia and Australia.

APLOMADO FALCON

Adult perched, immature in flight

APLOMADO FALCON

Falco fusco-coerulescens septentrionalis Todd

Other Names. Femoral Falcon, Orange-chested Hobby.

The Aplomado Falcon, so far as our limited knowledge of its feeding habits would indicate, is a bird of negative economic importance, the beneficial species which it destroys probably being balanced by the injurious creatures it eats, but there certainly is no reason why it should be persecuted merely because it is a member of the Hawk family, and just as certainly *it should be protected* as a rare and interesting bird.

The strikingly marked and very attractive little Aplomado Falcon is limited in its distribution in the United States to a narrow strip of country near the Mexican border east of California, where it is found principally on the open plains, in regions more or less covered with mesquite, cactuses and yuccas, rather than in mountainous districts. It is a graceful easy bird in flight, lacking somewhat the speed and dash of the Duck Hawk, which it resembles in size and outline. It frequently alights on the bare ground or perches on a low bush, a yucca stalk or a low post, to watch for its prey; it also hunts upon the wing, often hovering briefly in one spot after the manner of its near relative, the Sparrow Hawk. Major Brooks (1933) says of this species in Texas, "this graceful Falcon is not much in evidence until a prairie fire is started on the wide coastal plain, when they quickly arrive, sweeping gracefully backwards and forwards in front of the advancing flames and deftly capturing the large green locusts that are driven to flight. These are eaten on the wing, the Falcon rising in the air as it picks its prey to pieces, returning to the lower level to resume its hunting as each capture is disposed of." W. H. Hudson (1920) says of the Argentine representative of this species, "it has a poor spirit—it never boldly and openly attacks any bird, except of the smallest species."

FEEDING HABITS

Not very much is known of the feeding habits of the Aplomado Falcon. A. K. Fisher (1893) says that its diet, "probably like that of the Pigeon Hawk, consists largely of small birds, insects, and mammals, though little is known positively in reference to it." C. E. Bendire (1892) says it feeds upon "small reptiles, mice and other rodents, grasshoppers and insects of various kinds, and occasionally a bird." A. P. Smith (1910) says it feeds upon lizards, snakes and locusts. Allan Brooks (1933) describes it capturing "large green locusts." Manuscript notes in the Bureau of Biological Survey state that J. S. Ligon examined two stomachs which held a Lark Bunting and a Lark Sparrow respectively, and that R. T. Kellogg examined one which held two dragonflies, a cricket, a Horned Lark, and some seeds (possibly from the crop of the Lark).

PIGEON HAWK

Adult male perched, female or immature in flight

Description—Length of male about 15 inches, length of female 17 to 18 inches; spread about 40 inches. Adult: Above plain bluish gray, somewhat barred across rump with whitish; primaries with several narrow white bars; secondaries less distinctly barred but with white edges which form a transverse band when the bird is perched; tail darkest toward end, crossed by about eight narrow white bars; side of head and moustache black; a white line over eye broadening and becoming tawny on back of head; throat and upper chest white; thighs and under tail coverts tawny or orange brown. Immature: Colors duller; back brownish; under parts more or less buffy; breast streaked with dusky or blackish.

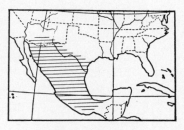

APLOMADO
FALCON
Ruled Area—Breeding Range

Range—"Arizona, New Mexico, and southern Texas south through Mexico" (A. O. U.). Representative races are found throughout South America.

PIGEON HAWKS
Falco columbarius LINNAEUS

While the Pigeon Hawks or American Merlins eat some injurious insects like grasshoppers and crickets, and occasionally eat destructive rodents, the great bulk of their food is composed of small birds, many of which are of decided benefit to agriculture or forestry, so that from a purely economic point of view little can be said in their favor. Their depredations upon poultry are negligible except in the vicinity of their northern breeding places. Elsewhere they are merely transient visitors which should not be persecuted, for the species is seldom common and, like its larger relative the Duck Hawk, the bird student finds it a most interesting bird to observe, because of its wildness, beauty and spectacular flight.

The Pigeon Hawk is a typical small Falcon, showing considerable resemblance to the Duck Hawk in color and habits but being noticeably smaller. It is northern or Canadian in its distribution, the eastern form barely entering the United States as a breeding bird in northern Maine and Michigan while the western forms are limited in the states, in the breeding season, to the high mountain country.

Except in its northern breeding range in the wooded regions across Canada, the Pigeon Hawk is best known as a migrant, following the passing flocks of small Shorebirds along our coasts and river valleys, or taking toll from the migrating hordes of Sparrows and Warblers and such "small fry." It is a fearless little Falcon, often surprisingly tame and unsuspicious in the presence of Man. Its flight suggests that of the larger Duck Hawk, but it is not quite so powerful or rapid. Occasionally it watches for its prey from a bare stub in a commanding position but more often it hunts on the wing. It sometimes soars for a short time, and it suggests the Sparrow Hawk in its habit of occasionally hovering briefly in one spot with rapidly beating wings, and also in its habit of pumping or "jetting" its tail once or twice immediately after it alights on a branch. It is easily distinguished from the Sparrow Hawk, however, by the absence of chestnut areas and the characteristic head markings of the latter bird, which it slightly exceeds in size.

Young Pigeon Hawks are very much like young Duck Hawks except for size and a less conspicuous moustache, but the adult male Pigeon Hawk is quite different from the adult Duck Hawk, especially on the under parts. The Duck Hawk and the paler Prairie Falcon are both larger than the Pigeon Hawk, which most nearly corresponds in size with the Sharp-shinned Hawk; the latter bird, however, has an entirely different silhouette, with short round-ended wings and long tail instead of the long and pointed falconine wings of the Pigeon Hawk. When perched, the closed wings of the Pigeon Hawk reach nearly to the end of the bird's tail while those of the Sharp-shin reach only to about the upper third of the tail.

FEEDING HABITS

The Pigeon Hawk is a confirmed bird killer which only occasionally catches other forms of food. B. H. Warren (1890) says, "in the few examinations which have been able to make of these hawks, only the remains of birds—pigeons and sparrows—have been detected." N. S. Goss (1891) says it "feeds largely upon the grasshoppers and lizards of the plains" in Kansas, but also speaks of its "killing readily the Passenger Pigeon, one of the swiftest of birds." W. E. D. Scott (1892) says that in Jamaica it takes "doves and smaller birds as well as lizards and such 'small deer.'" A. K. Fisher (1893) says its diet consists "mainly of small and medium-sized birds, insects, and occasionally small mammals," and that "pigeons,

RESULTS OF EXAMINATIONS OF STOMACHS AND CROPS

Authority	Number Examined	Mammals	Poultry or Game	Other Birds	Other Vertebrates	Insects	Miscellaneous	Empty
Aughey, Samuel, 1878 . . .	2	0	0	2	0	2	0	0
Fisher, A. K., 1893	60	2	2	43	0	17	0	16
Brewster, William, 1925 . .	4	0	0	3	0	2	0	0
Bailey, H. H., 1925	1	0	0	0	0	1	0	0
McLean, D. D., 1928-b . . .	9	0	0	18	0	0	0	0
Miller, W. DeW., mss., 1929.	16	0	0	17	0	7	0	0
Munro, J. A., 1929	2	0	0	2	0	0	0	0
Bur. Biol. Surv., 1893-1931 . .	90	6	1	56	3	39	1	3
Totals	184	8	3	141	3	68	1	19

flickers and grackles are about as large birds as it usually attacks," though it occasionally takes young chickens. Hoyes Lloyd (1920) saw one eating a House Sparrow and a Pine Grosbeak but says it ignored Chickadees, Ruffed Grouse and Pigeons. M. Y. Williams (1922) saw one catch a Cliff Swallow on the wing, and I myself once saw one catch a small bat, which shows the bird's dexterity and skill as a hunter. W. L. Dawson (1923) says it occasionally catches grasshoppers and large dragonflies and he quotes J. H. Bowles who saw a Pigeon Hawk catch a Tree Swallow. J. D. Smith (*in litt.*, 1925) saw one eating a Chickadee. T. G. Pearson (1933-a) states that 41 stomachs from New Jersey held three mammals, 34 birds and 119 insects. A. L. and H. L. Ferguson (1922) report on 298 stomachs from Fisher's Island, N. Y., which held four mammals, 318 birds and 967 insects. L. L. Snyder (1932) examined 13 stomachs from Ontario: 89.2% of their food contents was bird remains; insects formed 10.8% of the material.

The Pigeon Hawk is represented by four races in North America, according to the Check-List of the American Ornithologists' Union (1931). J. L. Peters (1931) believes it to be specifically identical with the European Merlin, *Falco aesalon aesalon* TUNSTALL, which he calls *Falco columbarius aesalon*, and assigns seven races to northern Europe and Asia.

EASTERN PIGEON HAWK
Falco columbarius columbarius LINNAEUS
Other Names. American Merlin, Blue Bullet, Little Corporal, Bullet Hawk, Pigeon Falcon.

Description—Length of male 10 to 10.5 inches, spread 23.5 to 26 inches; length of female 12 to 13.5 inches, spread about 24 to 26.5 inches. Adult male: Above slate blue with black shaft-streaks; neck a little rusty appearing; tail with three or four grayish white bars and a white tip; primaries barred with whitish; under parts varying from cream buff to ochraceous, heavily streaked with blackish except on throat which is usually unmarked white; "pantaloons" rufous in old birds. Adult female and immature: Upper parts dark brown or fuscous, neck streaked with lighter; tail with three or four yellowish or whitish bars and with a white tip; under parts as in adult male.

PIGEON HAWKS
Ruled Area—Breeding Range
Dotted Lines—Boundaries of
Winter Range

Range—"Breeds from the limit of trees in eastern Canada south to Newfoundland, Nova Scotia, New Brunswick, northern Maine, Ontario, northern Michigan, and southern Manitoba west to the eastern border of the Great Plains. Winters from the Gulf States south through eastern Mexico to Ecuador and northern Venezuela, and in the West Indies" (A. O. U.). Bermuda (Bradlee).

BLACK PIGEON HAWK
Falco columbarius suckleyi RIDGWAY
Other Names. Black Merlin, Suckley's Merlin, Suckley's Pigeon Hawk.

Description—This is the dark form of the American Merlin, found in the humid regions near the coast of British Columbia. "All the dark colors are sootier and more extensive. The back of the adult male is much like that of the Eastern Pigeon Hawk, but blacker, and that of the juvenile is nearly black instead of dark brown. Below, in all plumages, the dark stripes are deeper in color, broader and sharper in outline, and predominate over the lighter ground. The

MERLIN (left) and KESTREL (right)

Adult males

throat is generally plainly streaked instead of immaculate" (P. A. Taverner, 1926). The primaries are spotted, not barred, with whitish.

Range—"Breeds apparently in western British Columbia and perhaps on Vancouver Island. Winters in the coast region of British Columbia, rarely south to northern California." (A. O. U.)

RICHARDSON'S PIGEON HAWK
Falco columbarius richardsoni RIDGWAY
Other Names. Pale Merlin, Pale Pigeon Hawk, Richardson's Merlin.

Description—Much lighter colored than *F. c. columbarius* and more like the European Merlin, *Falco aesalon aesalon.* The adult male has the upper parts pearl gray; the brown of all plumages has a bleached appearance in comparison with the Eastern Pigeon Hawk; the tail is crossed by five or six narrow light bands; both the inner and outer webs of the primaries are banded with white; the crown is noticeably light colored.

Range—"Breeds in the Great Plains region from southern Alberta and southern Saskatchewan to northern Montana and northwestern North Dakota. Winters south through Colorado, New Mexico, and western Texas to northwestern Mexico." (A. O. U.)

WESTERN PIGEON HAWK
Falco columbarius bendirei SWANN
Other Name. Bendire's Merlin.

Description—"Similar to the eastern race (*columbarius*) but male lighter above; tail black, with three bands of grayish white (instead of slate-gray); female similar to *richardsoni* above, but a shade darker brown." (A. H. Howell, 1932.)

Range—"Breeds from northwestern Alaska, Yukon, and northwestern Mackenzie to British Columbia, northern and western Alberta, northern Saskatchewan, and south in the mountains to northern California. Winters south through California and New Mexico to the Cape region of Lower California and northwestern Mexico. Casual in Louisiana, Florida, North Carolina, and South Carolina." (A. O. U.)

MERLIN
Falco aesalon aesalon TUNSTALL

The European Merlin is very similar in appearance and actions to the American Pigeon Hawk, the principal difference in coloration being in the tail markings. As it is included in the North American avifauna only on the basis of its accidental occurrence in Greenland, little need be said about it here. It feeds very largely upon small birds up to the size of the European Partridge. W. H. Hudson (1895) says, "it preys chiefly on small birds and it was formerly trained to pursue snipe, pigeons, larks, blackbirds, etc." Although it is a destroyer of valuable small birds, it probably fills a definite niche in maintaining the balance of Nature in its haunts in the Eastern Hemisphere, but it need not be considered from an economic standpoint in the Western Hemisphere.

Description—Length 11 to 14 inches, spread 24 to 27 inches. Much like the American Pigeon Hawk, *Falco columbarius*, but male with a broad black subterminal band on the bluish gray tail of the adult, and about six narrow concealed bars; below light rusty streaked with brownish; female has upper parts brownish and lower parts paler than in male.

Range—"Breeds in northern Europe, Iceland, and the Faroes. Winters in Africa. Accidental in Greenland." (A. O. U.) Note: This bird is included in the fourth edition of the Check-List of the American Ornithologists' Union (1931) on the basis of a single specimen collected at Cape Farwell in Greenland, May 3, 1875, which has generally been considered as belonging to this subspecies. F. C. R. Jourdain (1933) says that Schioler assigns this specimen to the Iceland race of the Pigeon Hawk, *Falco columbarius subaesalon* BREHM, so that there is some question whether the European Merlin can be considered properly as a North American species, but as we are considering the Check-List as our authority on all matters of nomenclature, etc., it is here included.

KESTREL

Falco tinnunculus tinnunculus LINNAEUS

Other Name. Windhover.

The European Kestrel is much like our American Sparrow Hawk in actions and in general coloration, but it is decidedly larger and lacks the characteristic head markings of the latter bird, and the tail and rump are slaty or bluish gray instead of chestnut. It is a rare straggler to Greenland but as it has also appeared once in Massachusetts, it may appear again.

Like its close relative, the American Sparrow Hawk, the Kestrel is very largely beneficial in its feeding habits. W. E. Collinge (1924–1927), the English authority on economic ornithology, reports, on the basis of eighty stomach examinations and many pellet examinations, that the food of the Kestrel is about 89.5% beneficial, 4.5% neutral, and 6% injurious to Man's interests. He gives its animal food as consisting of about 64.5% destructive rodents, 14.5% birds, 16.5% injurious insects, 1% batrachians, 2.5% earthworms. Dr. Collinge adds, "it is a bird certainly deserving of very strict protection."

Description—Length 12.5 to 15.5 inches, spread about 27 to 30 inches. Adult male: Head, nape, rump, upper tail coverts and tail largely slaty bluish; back and shoulders (saddle) reddish brown or pale chestnut red, barred with black; flight feathers dark grayish brown, barred with white and reddish brown on inner webs; tail with a broad black subterminal band and white tip; under parts light yellowish or pale buff with blackish shaft-streaks, becoming broad arrowheads on flanks and belly, etc. Adult female and immatures: Reddish brown above, streaked with black on head and nape and barred on back; below as in adult male but leg feathers more heavily barred.

Range—"Northern part of the Eastern Hemisphere. Accidental in Massachusetts—and Greenland—." (A. O. U.)

Twelve Old World races of *Falco tinnunculus* are recognized by J. L. Peters (1931).

NORTH AMERICAN SPARROW HAWKS

Falco sparverius LINNAEUS

Other Names. American Kestrel, Killy Hawk, Windhover, Grasshopper Hawk, Mouse Hawk.

The Sparrow Hawks are the smallest and most brightly colored of our North American Hawks. The name is an unfortunate one, for birds form but a very small part of their food, and the European Sparrow Hawk is an Accipiter, closely related to our Sharp-shinned Hawk. The bad reputation of the European bird has been unjustly transmitted to our dainty little Falcon. The European Kestrel much more nearly corresponds with the American Sparrow Hawk in appearance and in habits. The name Killy Hawk, commonly applied to our bird because of its well-known notes, would be a much more appropriate name for the species.

Under ordinary conditions and in most places, *the Sparrow Hawk should be ranked as a decidedly beneficial species*, well deserving complete protection at all times. Dr. Fisher (1893) stated the case clearly when he said: "The Sparrow Hawk is almost exclusively insectivorous except when insect food is difficult to obtain. —Rarely do they touch any other kind of food until, either by the advancing season or other natural causes, the grasshopper crop is so lessened that their hunger cannot be appeased without undue exertion." The Sparrow Hawk, like most Raptors, is an opportunist and in cold weather, when insects are dead or dormant, must support life with other kinds of food.

The diminutive Sparrow Hawk is the only American member of the Hawk tribe which has taken at all kindly to civilization, if we except the Turkey and Black Vultures, which are common sights in the streets and on the roofs of buildings in many southern cities and towns, and the Osprey, which occasionally accepts as a nesting place a cart-wheel mounted on a tall pole by some coast-dwelling farmer. While almost every other species of Hawk has diminished very appreciably in numbers in recent years, the little Killy Hawk has probably increased in some parts of the country at least. William Brewster (1906) says: "The pretty little Sparrow Hawk has apparently added itself to our local summer fauna within comparatively recent times. At least the earliest record of its breeding within the Cambridge [Massachusetts] region of which I have any knowledge is that which was established by the finding of a nest at Waverley on May 26, 1877. Previous to that year we had seen the bird only during migration when it was somewhat less common than the Pigeon Hawk." Eleven years later a second nest was found and in 1889 a third nest. "After this the birds increased in numbers and extended their local distribution. Since 1895 they have bred more or less regularly at six or seven different places in Cambridge, Belmont and Watertown." And Thomas Nuttall

AMERICAN SPARROW HAWK

Male perched at left, female at right

(1832), writing one hundred years ago of that same Cambridge region, plainly knew very little about this species at first hand and remarks, "nor do they seem at all to visit the maritime provinces of New England." But today the Sparrow Hawk is a very familiar sight in the heart of the city of Cambridge, nesting in many places in church spires and under the eaves of residences and of the buildings of Harvard University and I have myself seen the birds many times flying about the grounds of the Museum of Comparative Zoology or using the tower of Memorial Hall as an observation point from which to sally forth after grasshoppers or House Sparrows.

The Sparrow Hawk is fond of perching on dead stubs, telephone posts or even fence posts when watching for its prey. Its straightaway flight is rapid, with a winnowing action of the slender pointed wings, but at some times its flight is light and wavering as if it had not decided just where it wanted to go. When a grasshopper, cricket or field mouse is located it often hovers for some time in one spot, with rapidly vibrating wings, before dropping on its prey or passing on, and it also sometimes poises, with spread wings and tail, supported motionless by some unseen air current; it occasionally soars like a Buteo but usually for a short time only, its knife-like wings being better adapted for rapid flight. It is sometimes a rather noisy bird, its common call being a rapidly repeated *killee, killee, killee*. This is our only Hawk which commonly nests in holes in trees and it is said also to be the only one which will use a bird house for a nesting site.

Its small size, typical falconine outline, and bright colors, make the Sparrow Hawk one of our most easily recognized Raptors. The head markings of the Sparrow Hawk are unique, and the color of no other American Hawk approaches the bright chestnut of the upperparts of this little bird. While only very slightly smaller than its close relative the Pigeon Hawk, it is more slender appearing and its wings seem longer proportionately. It is very different in silhouette from the Sharp-shin, which is also about the same size, the latter having short, round-ended wings.

FEEDING HABITS

The Sparrow Hawk is one of the most useful of the entire Hawk tribe, for its food is very largely composed of injurious insects, with a fair proportion of destructive rodents and only a small toll taken from beneficial birds. It might well be known as the "Grasshopper Hawk" because of its great fondness for these enemies of agriculture. F. C. Pellett (1912) studied the feeding of the young in Iowa and says that "while grasshoppers and crickets formed a considerable portion of the food, mice apparently predominated during the entire time. A few striped ground squirrels were taken and an occasional small bird,—for the most part English Sparrows, though a few Black-throated Buntings and Song Sparrows were included." A. R. Sherman (1913) also studied the feeding of the young: material brought included 14 ground squirrels, ten meadow mice, 22 birds, and numerous insects. Alexander Wetmore (1917) says they feed largely upon lizards in Porto Rico. Paul Bonnot (1921) saw a Sparrow Hawk alight on a Cliff Swallow's nest, reach in, and pull out an adult bird. W. L. Dawson (1923) says that on the Pacific coast they feed upon Meadowlarks, Brewer's Blackbirds, meadow mice, shrews, grasshoppers, beetles and crickets, spiders, lizards and small snakes. Thomas Hallinan (1924) says that in Panama they feed on small spiders, grasshoppers, iguanas and ground lizards. William Brewster (1925) says, "I have found only grasshoppers in their stomachs" in Maine. H. H. Bailey (1925) found only insects in more than a score of stomach examinations and says he has never known them to strike a bird, in Florida. John Steidl (1928) saw a Sparrow Hawk several times with two-weeks'-old chickens in its talons. P. L. Errington (*in litt.*, 1930) studied material from a nest and field observations, which included 21 rodents, five English Sparrows, and a great number of grasshoppers, June bugs, etc. L. L. Snyder (1932) examined 27 stomachs from Ontario: three were empty; rodents formed 25.8% of the food; bird remains, 6.9%; insects, 67.3%. G. M. Wright (1932) saw a Desert Sparrow Hawk "pursue, capture and devour a small bat." T. S. Roberts (1932) says that the superintendent of a game farm in Minnesota reported that a single pair of Sparrow Hawks took 52 young Ring-necked Pheasants in one week while feeding their young, which if authentic is most unusual. Dr. Roberts himself watched a brood of young which were fed almost entirely upon dragonflies during the two days they were under observation, although a half-grown striped gopher was also brought to them. T. G. Pearson (1933-a) states that five stomachs from New Jersey held two birds and 75 insects, and (1933-b) that 25 stomachs from Ohio held 13 mammals, one bird, 19 insects, and a crayfish, while two were empty.

RESULTS OF EXAMINATIONS OF STOMACHS AND CROPS

AUTHORITY	Number Examined	Mammals	Poultry or Game	Other Birds	Other Vertebrates	Insects	Miscellaneous	Empty
King, F. H., 1882	7	2	0	0	0	7	0	0
Warren, B. H., 1890	65	32	0	11	0	23	0	0
Fisher, A. K., 1893	320	101	0	54	12	215	29	29
Bailey, B. H., 1918	9	4	0	3	1	3	0	0
Brodkorb, Pierce, 1928	2	0	0	0	0	2	0	0
Miller, W. DeW., mss., 1929	13	0	0	0	0	13	0	0
Munro, J. A., 1929	5	2	0	1	0	6	1	0
Godsey, Townsend, 1931	6	6	0	0	0	0	0	0
Totals	427	147	0	69	13	269	30	29

The American Sparrow Hawk, *Falco sparverius*, is widely distributed throughout all but the Arctic regions of the Western Hemisphere. J. L. Peters (1931) recognizes twenty-three subspecies, four of which are included in the Check-List of the American Ornithologists' Union as found in North America.

EASTERN SPARROW HAWK
Falco sparverius sparverius LINNAEUS

Description—Length of male 8.75 to 10.5 inches, spread 20 to 22 inches; length of female

9 to 12 inches, spread 23 to 24.5 inches. Adult male: Upper parts chestnut or cinnamon reddish, back with black bars; top of head ashy blue with chestnut crown patch; cheeks and throat white; a black line extending down below the eye, another at rear of ear coverts and three other black patches on sides and back of nape, forming a broken chain of very characteristic markings; wing coverts and secondaries ashy blue spotted with black, primaries blackish, barred black and white on inner webs; rump and tail chestnut, the latter with white tip and broad subterminal band of black, outer tail-feathers black and white; breast tawny or buffy becoming whitish on belly, spotted more or less with black; cere, legs and feet bright yellow. Adult female:

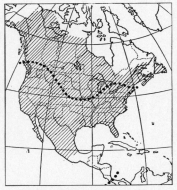

**NORTH AMERICAN
SPARROW HAWKS**
Ruled Area—Breeding Range
Dotted Line—Boundaries of
Winter Range

Head markings much as in male; back, wing-coverts, secondaries and tail duller chestnut narrowly cross-barred with black; underparts streaked, not spotted, with dark brown. Immature: Closely resemble adults of same sex.

Range—"Breeds from the Upper Yukon, British Columbia, northwestern Mackenzie, Alberta, Saskatchewan, Manitoba, northern Ontario, southern Quebec, and Newfoundland south to northwestern California, western Oregon, Colorado, eastern Texas, and the eastern Gulf States (except the southern border and Florida). Winters from southern British Columbia, Kansas, Indiana, central Illinois, Ohio, southern Ontario, southern Michigan, southern Vermont, and Massachusetts south through eastern Mexico to Panama" (A. O. U.). "Accidental in Denmark" (F. C. R. Jourdain, 1933). Bermuda (Bradlee).

DESERT SPARROW HAWK
Falco sparverius phalaena (Lesson)
Other Name. Pale Sparrow Hawk.

Description—Larger and paler than *F. s. sparverius*, with relatively longer tail, a larger crown patch, and more rufous than chestnut.

Range—"Breeds from southern New Mexico, Arizona, southern California, and southern Nevada south into Mexico and northern Lower California. Winters south to Guatemala." (A. O. U.)

SAN LUCAS SPARROW HAWK
Falco sparverius peninsularis Mearns

Description—Smaller, paler in coloration, with a diminution of the extent of the black markings; bill proportionately larger than in *F. s. sparverius*.

Range—"Southern Lower California." (A. O. U.)

LITTLE SPARROW HAWK
Falco sparverius paulus (Howe and King)
Other Name. Florida Sparrow Hawk.

Description—Smaller and darker than *F. s. sparverius;* tail and wings shorter in proportion, bill large and heavy; "rufous of upper parts very dark."

Range—"Florida Peninsula and the southern portion of the Gulf States north to central Alabama." (A. O. U.)

APPENDIX I
STATE LAWS RELATING TO HAWKS

ALABAMA

None protected.

ARIZONA

No Hawks protected. All Vultures on protected list.

ARKANSAS

None protected with exception of Vultures.

CALIFORNIA

All protected with exception of Sharp-shinned Hawk, Cooper's Hawk and Duck Hawk.

COLORADO

All protected with exception of Sharp-shinned Hawk, Cooper's Hawk, Goshawk, Duck Hawk and Eagle.

CONNECTICUT

None protected with the exception of Fish Hawk and Vultures.

DELAWARE

None protected except Fish Hawk and Vultures.

FLORIDA

All protected with exception of Sharp-shinned Hawk, Cooper's Hawk, Goshawk and Vultures.

GEORGIA

None protected with exception of Vultures.

IDAHO

None protected with exception of Vultures.

ILLINOIS

All protected with exception of Cooper's Hawk, Sharp-shinned Hawk, Goshawk, Duck Hawk and Pigeon Hawk.

INDIANA

None protected with exception of Bald Eagle (by special Act).

IOWA

All protected with exception of Sharp-shinned Hawk and Cooper's Hawk.

KANSAS

All protected with exception of Goshawk, Cooper's Hawk, Sharp-shinned Hawk and Eagle.

KENTUCKY

All protected with exception of Sharp-shinned Hawk and Cooper's Hawk.

LOUISIANA

All protected with exception of Cooper's Hawk, Duck Hawk, Sharp-shinned Hawk and Turkey and Black Vultures.

MAINE

None protected with exception of Vultures and the Bald Eagle (by special Act).

MARYLAND

None protected.

MASSACHUSETTS

All protected with the exception of Sharp-shinned Hawk, Cooper's Hawk and Goshawk—except that "any wild bird" may be killed which "has damaged or is about to damage property."

MICHIGAN

None protected with exception of Vultures and Bald Eagle.

MINNESOTA

None protected with exception of Vultures.

MISSISSIPPI

All protected with exception of Cooper's Hawk, Duck Hawk and Sharp-shinned Hawk.

MISSOURI

All protected with exception of Goshawk, Cooper's Hawk and Sharp-shinned Hawk. Law provides, however, that a fifty-cent bounty may be paid on "Hawks." This feature has been construed by officials of Game Department as in direct conflict with the section of game law which protects all Hawks save three.

MONTANA

None protected save Vultures.

NEBRASKA

All protected with exception of Cooper's Hawk, Red-shouldered Hawk, Sharp-shinned Hawk, Sparrow Hawk, Pigeon Hawk and Goshawk.

NEVADA

None protected save Vultures, and "American Eagle" (by special Act).

NEW HAMPSHIRE

None protected save Vultures.

NEW JERSEY

All protected with exception of Goshawk, Cooper's Hawk and Sharp-shinned Hawk.

NEW MEXICO

None protected with the exception of Vultures.

NEW YORK

Species protected are: Fish Hawk, Bald and Golden Eagles, Broad-winged Hawk, Sparrow Hawk, Red-shouldered Hawk, Rough-legged Hawk, Duck Hawk and Vultures.

NORTH CAROLINA

All protected with exception of Cooper's Hawk, Sharp-shinned Hawk and Vultures.

NORTH DAKOTA

All protected with exception of Sharp-shinned Hawk and Cooper's Hawk.

OHIO

All protected with exception of "Chicken Hawk," "Blue Hawk," Cooper's Hawk and Sharp-shinned Hawk.

OKLAHOMA

None protected.

OREGON

All protected with exception of Duck Hawk, Western Goshawk, Cooper's Hawk, Sharp-shinned Hawk, and Prairie Falcon.

PENNSYLVANIA

Not protected: Goshawk, Sharp-shinned Hawk, Cooper's Hawk, Red-tailed Hawk, Red-shouldered Hawk, Broad-winged Hawk, Marsh Hawk, Rough-legged Hawk, Duck Hawk, Pigeon Hawk and Vultures.

RHODE ISLAND

None protected with exception of Fish Hawk.

SOUTH CAROLINA

All protected except Cooper's Hawk, Duck Hawk, Sharp-shinned Hawk and Vultures. (Bald Eagle is protected by special Act.)

SOUTH DAKOTA

All protected with exception of Sharp-shinned Hawk and Cooper's Hawk.

TENNESSEE

All protected with exception of Cooper's Hawk, Sharp-shinned Hawk and Turkey Vulture.

TEXAS

All protected except Goshawk, Cooper's Hawk, Sharp-shinned Hawk, Duck Hawk and Vultures.

UTAH

All protected with exception of Sharp-shinned Hawk, Goshawk, Cooper's Hawk and Prairie Falcon.

VERMONT

None protected with exception of Vultures and Eagles.

VIRGINIA

None protected.

WASHINGTON

All protected except Duck Hawk, Pigeon Hawk, Western Goshawk, Sharp-shinned Hawk and Prairie Falcon.

WEST VIRGINIA

None protected save Vultures.

WISCONSIN

All protected with exception of Sharp-shinned Hawk, Cooper's Hawk, and Goshawk.

WYOMING

No State law relating to non-game birds.

APPENDIX II
REFERENCE BIBLIOGRAPHY

ABBOTT, CLINTON GILBERT
1911 The Home Life of the Osprey.

ALLEN, ARTHUR AUGUSTUS; &
KNIGHT, H. K.
1913 The Duck Hawks of Taughannock Gorge. Bird-Lore, pp. 1–8.

ALLEN, CHARLES SLOVER
1892 Breeding Habits of the Fish Hawk on Plum Island, New York. Auk, pp. 313–321.

AMERICAN ORNITHOLOGISTS' UNION
1931 Check-List of North American Birds, Fourth Edition.

ARNOW, ISAAC FLOOD
1904 Capture of Krider's Hawk at St. Mary's, Georgia, Auk, pp. 277–278.

AUDUBON, JOHN JAMES
1831–1839 Ornithological Biography, or an Account of the Habits of the Birds of the United States of America.
1840–1844 The Birds of America.

AUGHEY, SAMUEL
1878 Notes on the Nature of the Food of the Birds of Nebraska. First Annual Report of the United States Entomological Commission for the Year 1877 Relating to the Rocky Mountain Locust. Appendix II.

AUSTIN, OLIVER LUTHER, JR.
1932 The Birds of Newfoundland Labrador. Memoirs of the Nuttall Ornithological Club, No. VII.

BAILEY, BERT HEALD
1918 The Raptorial Birds of Iowa. Iowa Geological Survey, Bulletin No. 6.

BAILEY, FLORENCE AUGUSTA MERRIAM
1902 Handbook of Birds of the Western United States.
1916 Meeting Spring Half Way. Condor, pp. 183–190.
1928 Birds of New Mexico.

BAILEY, HAROLD HARRIS
1925 Birds of Florida.

BAIRD, SPENCER FULLERTON
1859 Birds of the Boundary. United States and Mexican Boundary Survey, Vol. II.

BAIRD, SPENCER FULLERTON;
CASSIN, JOHN; &
LAWRENCE, GEORGE NEWBOLD
1858 Explorations and Surveys for a Railroad Route from the Mississippi River to the Pacific Ocean. Part II, Birds.

BALDWIN, SAMUEL PRENTISS;
KENDEIGH, S. C.; & FRANKS, R. W.
1932 The Protection of Hawks and Owls in Ohio. Ohio Jour. Sci., Vol. XXXII, No. 5, pp. 403–424.

BANGS, OUTRAM
1898 Some New Races of Birds from Eastern North America. Auk, pp. 173–183.

BARBOUR, THOMAS
1923 The Birds of Cuba. Memoirs of the Nuttall Ornithological Club, No. VI.

BARLOW, CHESTER
1897 Some Notes on the Nesting Habits of the White-tailed Kite. Auk, pp. 14–21.

BARTSCH, PAUL
1897 Summer Birds of the Oneota Valley. Iowa Ornithologist, pp. 53–54.

BAYNARD, OSCAR EDWARD
1909 Notes from Florida on *Catharista urubu*. Oologist, pp. 191–193.

BEAUPRE, EDWIN
1922 The Duck Hawk. Canadian Field Naturalist, pp. 33–35.

BENDIRE, CHARLES EMIL
1892 Life Histories of North American Birds. United States National Museum, Special Bulletin No. 1.

1895 Notes on the Ancient Murrelet (*Synthliboramphus antiquus*) by Chas. Littlejohn. Auk. pp. 270–278.

BENNERS, GEORGE B.

1887 A Collecting Trip in Texas. Ornithologist and Oologist, pp. 65–69.

BONNOT, PAUL

1921 Sparrow Hawk captures Swallow. Condor, p. 136.

BRANDT, HERBERT WILLIAM

1924 The Nesting of the Short-tailed Hawk. Auk, pp. 59–64.

BREWSTER, WILLIAM

1880 Prowess of the Bald Eagle (*Haliaeetus leucocephalus*). Bulletin of the Nuttall Ornithological Club, pp. 57–58.

1883 On a Collection of Birds lately made by Mr. F. Stephens in Arizona. Bulletin of the Nuttall Ornithological Club, pp. 21–36.

1906 The Birds of the Cambridge Region of Massachusetts. Memoirs of the Nuttall Ornithological Club, No. IV.

1925 The Birds of the Lake Umbagog Region of Maine. Bulletin of the Museum of Comparative Zoology, Vol. 66, part 2.

BRODKORB, PIERCE

1928 Notes on the Food of some Hawks and Owls. Auk, pp. 212–213.

BROOKS, ALLAN CYRIL

1922 Notes on the Abundance and Habits of the Bald Eagle in British Columbia. Auk, pp. 556–559.

1927 Can Hawks prevent Mouse Plagues? Condor, pp. 249–250.

1928 Should we protect the Marsh Hawk? American Game, pp. 88 and 91.

1933 Some Notes on the Birds of Brownsville, Texas. Auk, pp. 59–63.

BRYANT, HAROLD CHILD

1913 The Results of some Miscellaneous Stomach Examinations. Condor, pp. 92–93.

1918 Evidence on the Food of Hawks and Owls in California. Condor, pp. 126–127.

1921 Red-bellied Hawk eats Caterpillars. Condor, p. 65.

BURNS, FRANK LORENZO

1911 A Monograph of the Broad-winged Hawk (*Buteo platypterus*). Wilson Bulletin, pp. 139–320.

BURROWS, D. B.

1917 White-tailed Hawks (*Buteo albicaudatus*). Oologist, pp. 78–81.

BURTCH, VERDI

1927 Near Cannibalism in a Buteo. Auk, 248–249.

CAMERON, EWEN SOMERLED

1905 Nesting of the Golden Eagle in Montana. Auk, pp. 158–167.

1907 The Birds of Custer and Dawson Counties, Montana. Auk, pp. 241–270.

1908 Observations on the Golden Eagle in Montana. Auk, pp. 251–268.

1913 Notes on Swainson's Hawk (*Buteo swainsoni*) in Montana. Auk, pp. 167–176 and 381–394.

1914 The Ferruginous Rough-leg (*Archibuteo ferrugineus*) in Montana. Auk, pp. 159–167.

CHAMBERLAIN, MONTAGUE

1889 Some Account of the Birds of Southern Greenland, from the Mss. of A. Hagerup. Auk, pp. 291–297.

CHITTENDEN, FRANK HURLBUT

1911 Some Insects injurious to Truck Crops. United States Bureau of Entomology, Bull. No. 82, Part VII, p. 87.

CLARK, AUSTIN HOBART

1905 Birds of the Southern Lesser Antilles. Proceedings of the Boston Society of Natural History, Vol. 32, No. 7.

COALE, HENRY KELSO

1925 Habits of the Marsh Hawk. Auk, p. 269.

COLLINGE, WALTER EDWARD

1924–1927 The Food of some British Wild Birds.

COUES, ELLIOTT

1874 Birds of the Northwest: A Handbook of the Ornithology of the

Region drained by the Missouri River and its Tributaries. United States Geological Survey of the Territories, Miscellaneous Publications, No. 3.

1883 Note on the Mississippi Kite. Bulletin of the Nuttall Ornithological Club, p. 61.

1903 Key to North American Birds. Fifth edition.

CRABB, EDWARD DRANE

1921 Some Unexpected Findings in the Stomach Contents of Predatory Birds and Mammals. Proceedings of the Oklahoma Academy of Science, pp. 65–66.

1923 A Note on the Economic Status of the Bald Eagle in Alaska. Auk, pp. 419–423.

CRIDDLE, NORMAN

1912 The Marsh Hawk. Ottawa Naturalist, Vol. 25, pp. 147–151.

1915 Some Habits of the Swainson's Hawk in Manitoba. Ottawa Naturalist, Vol. 29, pp. 94–97.

1917 The Red-tailed Hawk in Manitoba. Ottawa Naturalist, Vol. 31, pp. 74–76.

DADISMAN, A. J.

1934 West Virginia Wild Life. April-May, p. 11.

DARCUS, SOLOMON JOHN

1930 Notes on the Birds of the Northern Part of the Queen Charlotte Islands in 1927. Canadian Field Naturalist, pp. 45–49.

DAWSON, WILLIAM LEON

1923 The Birds of California.

DEANE, RUTHVEN

1907 Unusual Abundance of the American Goshawk (Accipiter atricapillus). Auk, pp. 182–186.

DECKER, FRANK RUSSEL & BOWLES, J. H.

1930 The Prairie Falcon in the State of Washington. Auk, pp. 25–31.

DE GROOT, DUDLEY SARGENT

1927 The California Clapper Rail: Its Nesting Habits, Enemies and Habitat. Condor, pp. 259–270.

DICE, LEE RAYMOND

1920 Notes on some Birds of Interior Alaska. Condor, pp. 176–185.

DIXON, JAMES BENJAMIN

1928 Life History of the Red-bellied Hawk. Condor, pp. 228–236.

DIXON, JOSEPH SCATTERGOOD

1906 Land Birds of San Onofre, California. Condor, pp. 91–98.

1909 A Life History of the Northern Bald Eagle. Condor, pp. 187–193.

DUNN, JAMES OREGON

1895 Notes on some Birds of Northeastern Illinois. Auk, pp. 393–395.

FERGUSON, ALFRED LUDLOW; &
FERGUSON, HENRY LEE

1922 The Fall Migration of Hawks as observed at Fisher's Island, N. Y. Auk, pp. 488–496.

FINLEY, WILLIAM LOVELL

1905 Photographing the Aerie of a Western Red-tail. Condor, pp. 3–7.

FISHER, ALBERT KENDRICK

1893 The Hawks and Owls of the United States in their Relation to Agriculture. United States Department of Agriculture, Division of Ornithology and Mammalogy, Bulletin No. 3.

FORBUSH, EDWARD HOWE

1927 Birds of Massachusetts and other New England States. Part II.

FOWLER, FREDERICK HALL

1903 Stray Notes from Southern Arizona. Condor, pp. 68–71.

1931 Studies of the Food and Growth of a Prairie Falcon. Condor, pp. 193–201.

FRIEDMANN, HERBERT

1925 Notes on the Birds observed in the Lower Rio Grande Valley of Texas during May, 1924. Auk, pp. 537–554.

1934 The Siberian Rough-legged Hawk in Alaska. Condor, p. 246.

FULLER, ARTHUR BENNETT

1922 Notes from Essex, Massachusetts, 1921. Auk, p. 425.

GABRIELSON, IRA NOEL
1922 Some Hawks of Harney Valley, Oregon. Condor, pp. 33–34.

GANIER, ALBERT FRANKLIN
1902 The Mississippi Kite (*Ictinia misisippiensis*). Osprey, pp. 85-90.

GENTRY, THOMAS GEORGE
1877 Life Histories of the Birds of Eastern Pennsylvania. Vol. II.

GILBERT, CHARLES HENRY
1922 Kamchatka Sea Eagle at Kodiak, Alaska. Condor, p. 66.

GLOYD, HOWARD KAY
1925 Field Studies of the Diurnal Raptores of Eastern and Central Kansas. Wilson Bulletin, pp. 133–149.

GODSEY, TOWNSEND
1931 Missouri Game and Fish News.

GOSS, NATHANIEL STICKNEY
1891 History of the Birds of Kansas.

GREY, HENRY
1917 Zone-tailed Hawk at San Diego, California. Condor, p. 103.
1925 Some Unusual Birds at or near San Diego. Condor, p. 37.

GRINNELL, JOSEPH; &
STORER, TRACY IRWIN
1924 Animal Life in the Yosemite.

GROSS, ALBERT OTTO
1928 Progress Report of the New England Ruffed Grouse Investigation Committee.

GUTHRIE, JOSEPH EDWARD
1931 Red-shouldered Hawks and Chimney Swifts. Iowa Bird Life, p. 35.

HALLINAN, THOMAS
1924 Notes on some Panama Canal Zone Birds with Special Reference to their Food. Auk, pp. 304–326.

HANNA, G. DALLAS
1920 Additions to the Avifauna of the Pribilof Islands, Alaska, including Four Species new to North America. Auk, pp. 248–254.

HANNA, WILSON CREAL
1930 Notes on the Golden Eagle in Southern California. Condor, pp. 121–123.

HANTZCH, BERNHARD
1929 Contributions to the Knowledge of the Avifauna of Northeastern Labrador. Canadian Field Naturalist, pp. 11–18.

HENNING, CARL FRITZ
1896 Notes and News. Iowa Ornithologist, p. 85.

HENNINGER, WALTHER FRIEDRICH; &
JONES, LYNDS
1909 The Falcones of North America. Wilson Bulletin, pp. 205–218.

HENSHAW, HENRY WETHERBEE
1875 Report upon the Ornithological Collections made in Portions of Nevada, Utah, California, Colorado, New Mexico, and Arizona, during the Years 1871, 1872, 1873, and 1874. Wheeler's Report, Geographical and Geological Explorations West of the One Hundredth Meridian. Vol. V, pp. 131–507.

HERRICK, FRANCIS HOBART
1924 The Daily Life of the American Eagle: Late Phase. Auk, pp. 389–422 and 517–541.
1934 The American Eagle, a study in Natural and Civil History, pp. 72–73 and p. 236.

HERSEY, FRANK SEYMOUR
1923 A Nestling Red-shouldered Hawk's Hearty Meal. Auk, p. 693.

HOWELL, ARTHUR HOLMES
1924 Birds of Alabama.
1932 Florida Bird Life.

HUBBARD, RALPH
1920 Colorado Notes. Condor, pp. 37–38.

HUBER, WHARTON
1929 Zone-tailed Hawk in Lincoln Co., New Mexico. Auk, p. 544.

HUDSON, WILLIAM HENRY
1895 British Birds.
1920 Birds of La Plata.

HUEY, LAURENCE MARKHAM
1924 Notes from Southern and Lower California. Condor, pp. 74–75.

JENSEN, JENS KNUDSEN
1926 Red-tailed Hawk killing Snakes. Auk, pp. 368–369.

JEWETT, STANLEY GORDON
1926 The Prairie Falcon in the Willamette Valley, Oregon. Condor, p. 98.

JOURDAIN, FRANCIS CHARLES ROBERT
1933 On the Palaearctic Element in the A. O. U. "Check-List" (4th Edit.). Auk, pp. 201–204.

KALMBACH, EDWIN RICHARD
1927 Monetary Value of Marsh Hawks. Auk, pp. 100–101.

KENNARD, FREDERICK HEDGE
1894 The Habits and Individualities of the Red-shouldered Hawk (*Buteo lineatus*) in the Vicinity of Brookline, Mass. Auk, pp. 197–210.

KING, FRANKLIN HIRAM
1882 Economic Relations of Wisconsin Birds. Geology of Wisconsin, Vol. I.

KUSER, CYNTHIA DRYDEN
1929 An Osprey feeds on Ducks. Bird-Lore, pp. 260–261.

LANG, HERBERT
1924 Ampullarius and Rostrhamus at Georgetown, British Guiana. Nautilus, pp. 73–77.

LANO, ALBERT
1922 Golden Eagle (*Aquila chrysaëtos*) and Porcupine. Auk, pp. 258–259.

LAWRENCE, GEORGE NEWBOLD
1874 Birds of Western and Northwestern Mexico. Memoirs of the Boston Society of Natural History, Vol. II, pp. 265–319.
1875 Birds of Southwestern Mexico collected by Francis E. Sumichrast. United States National Museum, Bulletin 4.

LINCOLN, FREDERICK CHARLES
1920 Birds of the Clear Creek District, Colorado. Auk, pp. 60–77.

LINTON, C. B.
1907 Mexican Black Hawk in California. Condor, p. 110.

LLOYD, HOYES
1920 A Pigeon Hawk winters at Ottawa. Canadian Field Naturalist, p. 116.

LLOYD, WILLIAM
1887 Birds of Tom Green and Concho Counties, Texas. Auk, pp. 181–193.

LUTTRINGER, LEO AMOS, JR.
1930 The Goshawk Law. Cardinal, pp. 220–226.

MACMILLAN, DONALD B.
1918 Four Years in the White North.

MACPHERSON, H. B.
1910 The Home Life of a Golden Eagle.

MAYNARD, CHARLES JOHNSON
1881 The Birds of Eastern North America, with Original Descriptions of all the Species which occur East of the Mississippi River between the Arctic Circle and the Gulf of Mexico.

MCLEAN, DONALD DUDLEY
1928a White-tailed Kites near Hollister. California Fish and Game, p. 91.
1928b The Pigeon Hawk's Bill of Fare. California Fish and Game, pp. 171–173.
1932 Prairie Falcons. California Fish and Game, p. 97.

MEARNS, EDGAR ALEXANDER
1886 Some Birds of Arizona. Auk, pp. 60–73.

MERRIAM, CHARLES HART
1888 Grasshoppers and Hawks. Forest and Stream, Vol. 31, pp. 455–456.

MILLER, JOHN PAUL
1931 The Red-tailed Hawk (*Buteo borealis* [Gmelin]) in Relation to the Control of the Columbian Ground Squirrel (*Citellus c. columbianus* [Ord.]). Murrelet, pp. 46–49.

MILLER, LOYE HOLMES
1920 Notes from the Region of Lake Tahoe. Condor, pp. 78–79.

1925 Food of the Harris Hawk. Condor, pp. 71–72.
1926 The Food of a White-tailed Kite. Condor, pp. 172–173.
1930 Further Notes on the Harris Hawk. Condor, pp. 210–211.

MORGAN, A. P.
1896 The Myxomycetes of the Miami Valley, Ohio Journal of the Cincinnati Society of Natural History.

MORRIS, ROBERT OLIVER
1892 Notes from Springfield, Massachusetts. Auk, p. 74.

MUNRO, JAMES ALEXANDER
1929 Notes on the Food Habits of certain Raptores in British Columbia and Alberta. Condor, pp. 112–116.

MURDOCH, JOHN
1885 Report of the International Polar Expedition to Point Barrow, Alaska. Part IV, Natural History, pp. 89–128.

NASH, CHARLES WILLIAM
1898 The Birds of Ontario in Relation to Agriculture.

NAUMAN, EMIL DANTON
1929 The Raptor's Mistake. Wilson Bulletin, p. 252.

NEHRLING, HEINRICH
1882 List of Birds observed at Houston, Harris Co., Texas, and in the Counties of Montgomery, Galveston, and Ford Bend. Auk, pp. 166–175.

NELSON, EDWARD WILLIAM
1887 Report upon the Natural History Collections made in Alaska between the Years 1877 and 1881. Birds of Alaska. United States Signal Service, Arctic Series, No. 3.

NICHOLSON, DONALD JOHN
1928 Habits of the Black Vulture in Florida. Oologist, pp. 21–24.
1930 Habits of the Florida Red-shouldered Hawk. Wilson Bulletin, pp. 32–35.

NORTON, A. H. W.
1896 Audubon's Caracara, Polyborus cheriway (Jacq.). Wilson Bulletin, No. 7, pp. 1–3.

NUTTALL, THOMAS
1832 A Manual of the Ornithology of the United States and Canada.

NUTTING, CHARLES CLEVELAND
1882 On a Collection of Birds from the Hacienda "La Palma," Gulf of Nicoya, Costa Rica. Proceedings of the United States National Museum, pp. 382–409.

OBERHOLSER, HARRY CHURCH
1906 The North American Eagles and their Economic Relations. United States Department of Agriculture, Biological Survey, Bulletin No. 27.

OWEN, ROBERT
1860 On the Habits of the Swallow-tailed Kite (Elanoides furcatus) in Guatemala. Ibis, pp. 240–243.

PEARSON, THOMAS GILBERT
1919 The Turkey Vulture. Bird-Lore, pp. 319–322.
1930 The Red-tailed Hawk. National Association of Audubon Societies, Educational Leaflet No. 136.
1933a Cape May Hawk Investigation. Bird-Lore, pp. 73-74.
1933b Ohio Reports on Food Habits of Hawks and Owls. Bird-Lore, pp. 241–242.

PELLETT, FRANK C.
1912 Food Habits of the Red-tailed Hawk, Cooper Hawk, and Sparrow Hawk. Proceedings of the Iowa Academy of Science, pp. 199–201.

PETERS, JAMES LEE
1931 Check-List of Birds of the World. Vol. I.

PETERSON, ROGER TORY
1934 A Field Guide to the Birds giving Field Marks of all Species found in Eastern North America.

PICKWELL, GAYLE BENJAMIN
1930 The White-tailed Kite. Condor, pp. 221–239.

APPENDIX II

PIERCE, WRIGHT MCEWEN

1919 Miscellaneous Stomach Examinations. Condor, p. 127.

RAMSDEN, CHARLES THEODORE

1911 *Buteo platypterus* eating Minnows. Auk, p. 485.

REDINGTON, PAUL GOODWIN

1929 Usefulness of Hawks and Owls. Report of the Chief of the Bureau of Biological Survey, p. 9.

RICHARDS, VIOLA F.

1919 The Early History of a Duck Hawk. Auk, pp. 349–350.

RIDGWAY, ROBERT

1876 Ornithology of Guadalupe Island, based on Notes and Collections made by Dr. Edward Palmer. Bulletin of the United States Geological and Geographical Survey of the Territories, Vol. II, Bull. No. 2, pp. 183–197.

1877 Report on the United States Geological Exploration of the Fortieth Parallel. Volume 4, Part 3, Ornithology, pp. 303–643.

1885 Catalogue of a Collection of Birds made on the Island of Cozumel, Yucatan, by the Naturalists of the U. S. Fish Commission Steamer Albatross, Capt. Z. L. Tonner, Commander. Proceedings of the United States National Museum, Vol. VIII, pp. 560–583.

ROBERTS, THOMAS SADLER

1932 The Birds of Minnesota.

RODMAN, O. H. P.

1926 Terrestrial Habits of the Osprey. Forest and Stream, p. 356.

SAUNDERS, ARETAS ANDREWS

1911 A Preliminary List of the Birds of Gallatin County, Montana. Auk, pp. 26–49.

SCHUTZE, ADOLPH E.

1904 Nesting Habits of the Caracara. Condor, pp. 106–108.

SCOTT, WILLIAM EARL DODGE

1892 Observations on the Birds of Jamaica, West Indies. Auk, pp. 120–129.

SEEBOHM, HENRY

1883 History of British Birds.

SENNETT, GEORGE BURRITT

1879 Further Notes on the Ornithology of the Lower Rio Grande of Texas. Bulletin of the United States Geological and Geographical Survey of the Territories, Vol. V, pp. 371–440.

SHERMAN, ALTHEA ROSINA

1913 The Nest Life of the Sparrow Hawk. Auk, pp. 406–418.

SIMMONS, GEORGE FINLEY

1925 Birds of the Austin Region, Texas.

SINGLEY, JOHN ALLEN

1888 Birds and their Relation to Agriculture. Ornithologist and Oologist, pp. 24–25.

SMITH, AUSTIN PAUL

1910 Miscellaneous Bird Notes from the Lower Rio Grande. Condor, pp. 93–103.

1915 Birds of the Boston Mountains, Arkansas. Condor, pp. 41–57.

SMITH, LESTER WHEADON

1921 Records of Interest from Meriden, Connecticut. Auk, pp. 465–467.

SMYTH, ELLISON ADGER, JR.

1912 Birds observed in Montgomery County, Virginia. Auk, pp. 508–530.

SNYDER, LESTER LYNNE

1932 The Hawks and Owls of Ontario.

STEIDL, JOHN

1928 Sparrow Hawk killing young Chickens. Auk, p. 503.

STEJNEGER, LEONHARD

1885 Results of Ornithological Explorations in the Commander Islands and in Kamtschatka. United States National Museum, Bull. 29.

STODDARD, HERBERT LEE

1931 The Bobwhite Quail, its Habits, Preservation and Increase.

STONE, WITMER

1908 Birds of New Jersey, pp. 159–160.

1924 The Mississippi Kite (*Ictinia misissippiensis*) at Cape May, N. J. Auk, pp. 477–478.

STONER, EMERSON AUSTIN

1933 The White-tailed Kite at Benicia, California. Condor, p. 121.

SUMNER, EUSTACE LOWELL, JR.

1929 Comparative Studies in the Growth of Young Raptores. Condor, pp. 85–111.

SUTTON, GEORGE MIKSCH

1927 The Invasion of Goshawks and Snowy Owls during the Winter of 1926–1927. Cardinal, pp. 35–41.

1928 Notes on a Collection of Hawks from Schuylkill County, Pennsylvania. Wilson Bulletin, pp. 84–95.

1929a Hawks and Owls—Friends or Foes? Saturday Evening Post, Nov. 16, 1929.

1929b How can the Bird-Lover help to save the Hawks and Owls? Auk, pp. 190–195.

1931 The Status of the Goshawk in Pennsylvania. Wilson Bull., pp. 108–113.

1932 Exploration of Southampton Island, Hudson Bay.

SWARTH, HARRY SCHELWALDT

1905 Summer Birds of the Papago Indian Reservation and the Santa Rita Mountains, Arizona. Condor, pp. 22–28.

1920 Birds of the Papago Saguaro National Monument and the Neighboring Region, Arizona.

1924 Fall Migration Notes from the San Francisco Mountain Region, Arizona. Condor, pp. 183–190.

TAVERNER, PERCY ALGERNON

1919 The Birds of the Red Deer River, Alberta. Auk, pp. 1–21.

1926 Birds of Western Canada.

TAYLOR, ALEXANDER O'DRISCOLL

1892 Occurrence of the Black Gyrfalcon in Rhode Island. Auk, pp. 300–301.

THAYER, GERALD HANDERSON

1904 A Massachusetts Duck Hawk Aery. Bird-Lore, pp. 47–53.

THOMAS, GERALD BAMBER

1908 The Mexican Black Hawk. Condor, pp. 116–118.

THORBURN, ARCHIBALD

1925–1926 British Birds, Vol. II.

TOWNSEND, CHARLES WENDELL; &

BENT, ARTHUR CLEVELAND

1910 Additional Notes on the Birds of Labrador. Auk, pp. 1–18.

TURNER, LUCIEN MCSHAN

1886 Contributions to the Natural History of Alaska. Part V. Birds.

TYLER, CHARLES GRIPPER

1923 Observations on the Habits of the Prairie Falcon. Condor, pp. 90–97.

URNER, CHARLES ANDERSON

1925 Notes on Two Ground-nesting Birds of Prey. Auk, pp. 31–41.

VAN KAMMEN, I. J.

1916 Relative to the Bald Eagle in Alaska. Oologist, pp. 156–158.

WARREN, BENJAMIN HARRY

1890 Report on the Birds of Pennsylvania.

WAYNE, ARTHUR TREZEVANT

1910 Birds of South Carolina.

WETMORE, ALEXANDER

1909 Fall Notes from Eastern Kansas. Condor, pp. 154–164.

1917 The Birds of Culebra Island, Porto Rico. Auk, pp. 51–62.

WILLETT, GEORGE

1914 Birds of Sitka and Vicinity, Alaska. Condor, pp. 71–91.

WILLIAMS, MERTON YARWOOD

1922 Biological Notes along Fourteen Hundred Miles of the Mackenzie River System. Canadian Field Naturalist, pp. 61–66.

WILSON, ALEXANDER

1831 American Ornithology.

WORTHINGTON, WILLIS WOODFORD

1899 Rare Birds on Eastern Long Island. Auk, p. 85.

WRIGHT, GEORGE MELENDEZ

1932 A Bat-eating Sparrow Hawk. Condor, p. 43.